REMIN
OF SHIBUYA
1929-1938

To Kathy

With warmest regards,
love
9/19/2019
Yumi

Yumi Hosono

LINUS
Learning

Published by Linus Learning

Ronkonkoma, NY 11779

ISBN 10: 1-60797-525-4

ISBN 13: 978-1-60797-525-0

Printed in the United States of America.

This book is printed on acid-free paper.

Print Number   5   4   3   2   1

To Hachiko

and

all animal lovers

The true story of the loyal dog Hachiko and life in Tokyo in the 1930s

Front cover photo: *Yukiko and Kinuko in Tokyo circa 1934.*
Back cover photo: *The postcards Yukiko received from her French friend.*

Praise for *Reminiscence of Shibuya* 1929-1938

"Yumi Hosono, a student of mine at NYU, has written a memoir of her family's life in Shibuya, Tokyo, during the years 1929-1938. The small book is anchored by the heartwarming story of the legendary Hachiko, an Akita dog, known throughout Japan and the West (cf. "Hachi, A Dog's Tale" starring Richard Gere) for its faithfulness. Adopted in 1924 by a university professor who died a year later, Akita, with his endearing cocked ear, became a symbol for loyalty, when he continued waiting at Shibuya Station for the return of his master from work for 10 full years. Yumi's book gives at the same time a vivid picture of what was at that time a rapidly-changing city with all its beautiful traditions, and is now, with one of Tokyo's busiest railway stations, an area known as one of the fashion centers of Japan."

Géza von Habsburg, Ph.D, Archduke of Austria,
Art historian and Art curator

"Yumi Hosono's portrait of her family and their social world in the Shibuya district of Tokyo during the 1930s offers a fascinating window on modern Japan. The cosmopolitanism and affluence of this corner of Tokyo in the years before World War II contrast sharply with common images of the era. In addition to stories of the city and of fashions in art and architecture, we learn of the deep relationship between Japanese and Turkish elites, of Japanese aristocrats entertaining Hollywood stars, and of Helen Keller's visit to Japan. This is a book filled with surprises."

Jordan Sand, Professor of Japanese History at
Georgetown University

"In this lovely book, Yumi Hosono has woven many silken threads into a beautiful tapestry of love, faithfulness and honor wrapped around the tale of Hatchiko, a dog who became a legend in Japan because of his steadfast loyalty and great heart.

In retelling Hatchiko's story, in *Reminiscence of Shibuya,* Yumi has captured the spirit of a long ago time in Japan that most of us have never glimpsed... a time of graciousness, dignity and honor, steeped in the ancient Samurai tradition. She has woven in her own family history to give us a window into a unique moment in time from a very human perspective. She also recounts how Helen Keller fell in love with an Akita puppy during her travels in Japan and brought him back to her home in Connecticut, introducing the breed to America.

I was enchanted by all of it ...I think you will be, too."

Cathy Cash Spellman, author of *Paint the Wind* and
Bless the Child

Table of Content

Who is Hachiko?...ix

Prologue...x

Map of Japan xiii

Map of Tokyo xiv

Characters xv

CHAPTER 1
The Encounter with Hachiko 1

CHAPTER 2
Zeppelin in Shibuya Sky 11

CHAPTER 3
Grandmother and Old Tales.. 24

CHAPTER 4
Yukiko's House and Frequent Meeting
with Hachiko...37

CHAPTER 5
Noel Nouet and Foreigners in Tokyo 49

CHAPTER 6
Mansions in Tokyo 57

CHAPTER 7
Statue of Hachiko and Pilgrim Dogs............................70

CHAPTER 8
Friendship with Turkish People....................................80

CHAPTER 9
Architecture of Tokyo 90

CHAPTER 10
The Last Garden Party.. 97

CHAPTER 11
Hachiko Passes Away 105

CHAPTER 12
Turkish Ambassador 110

CHAPTER 13
Ertuğrul Monument Unveiling Ceremony....................121

CHAPTER 14
Helen Keller and Akita Dogs 124

CHAPTER15
1938...130

CHAPTER 16
Departure.. 136

Epilogue 142
Acknowledgment 145
Glossary 146
Reference Materials 151
Credit and Courtesy... 152

Who is Hachiko?

Hachiko was an Akita dog born in Odate, Akita in 1923. He was adopted by Professor Hidesaburo Ueno in 1924 in Shibuya. He was named 'Hachi' (eight in Japanese) because when he was standing, his two legs looked like the shape of the Chinese character eight (八). It spreads out like an unfolded fan and it means prosperity. The ko (公) is an honorific or friendly suffix. Hachiko always accompanied professor Ueno. He went to see the professor Ueno off at Shibuya station in the morning and came back to meet him there in the evening. However, when his master suddenly passed away at the university in 1925, Hachiko didn't understand that and kept waiting for him at Shibuya station for 10 years until his own death.

Figure 1: Hachiko.

Prologue

Everything in this story is based on facts told to me by my mother, Yukiko. I used my imagination to create some of the scenes. However, the characters, places, and events are all real. My mother Yukiko lived near Shibuya. My mother and her sisters took a red streetcar to school from 1930. When they got off at a plaza in front of Shibuya station, they saw Hachiko waiting for professor Ueno by the ticket gate every day. Sometimes they patted him. He showed affection to those who loved him. His fur was thick and coarse. His curled white fluffy tail looked beautiful on his light brown back. He had very gentle eyes. My mother saw Hachiko there from 1929 until 1935 when he passed away.

***

In 2007, we found old undeveloped film and glass negatives that my grandfather took in the 1930s at my parents' house. Even my mother was unaware that those undeveloped negatives had been saved for such a long time. My mother's house in Tokyo Setagaya district was almost burnt down by the March 10, 1945 Tokyo air raid, but miraculously survived. However, my mother's family moved their possessions to their relatives' house in the suburbs and that house was completely burnt down along with all of the family heirlooms. It is a mystery how these negatives survived. We suppose that they were kept in the drawer of my grandfather's desk, which eventually was moved to my parents' house.

We had a professional film laboratory develop the negatives. A few days later the images of my mother's childhood life in the late 1920s and 1930s appeared. In her time, cameras were rare in Japan, and taking family pictures was quite special. My grandfather took them, to record their daily lives.

When my mother revisited the photos, they brought her childhood memories back to life. She remembered the vivid image of Hachiko with one bent ear; something that made a lasting impression on her. It was then that her childhood story began to pour out of her.

Tokyo was an international city back then. By the efforts of the residents, the city miraculously recovered from the damage of the Great Kanto Earthquake of 1923. Modern architecture, elegant shops, and western restaurants flourished. It was the second megacity in the world; after New York. Scenery from the traditional Edo Era (1603 to 1868) still existed everywhere. The magical mixture of the old and the new, the east and west, attracted people from all over the world. They came to live in this exciting city, the imperial capital of Tokyo.

The 1929 worldwide depression, of course, had a huge impact on Japan. However, Japanese people still sought new technology and enjoyed exciting art during the short peaceful period that was sandwiched between two world wars. It was a belle époque of Japan.

**

I published a book in Japanese in 2008. Even the Japanese people didn't know about this international period of Tokyo. They found it eye-opening. Then I thought it would be something many foreigners might find interesting as well: this fleeting and fascinating moment in the history of the country. So I rewrote it in English. I included some photos by my grandfather and others that I borrowed from museums or institutions.

I fervently hope you will enjoy reading about the birth of a great metropolis...where a faithful dog waited patiently for his master.

Map of Japan

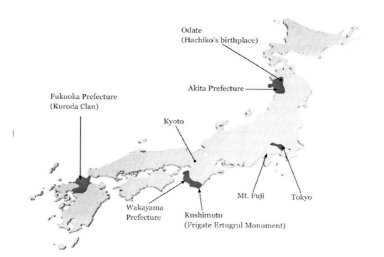

Odate
(Hachiko's birthplace)

Akita Prefecture

Fukuoka Prefecture
(Kuroda Clan)

Kyoto

Wakayama
Prefecture

Kushimoto
(Frigate Ertugrul Monument)

Mt. Fuji

Tokyo

Map of Tokyo

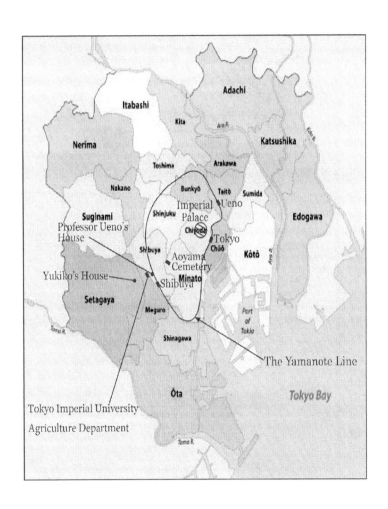

Characters

Colonel Ryusuke Yonezawa: Imperial Japanese army officer, diplomat and author, Yukiko's father

Yukiko Yonezawa: Main character, author's mother

Motoko Yonezawa: Ryusuke's wife, Yukiko and other children's mother

Tei Yonezawa: Ryusuke's mother, Yukiko and other children's grandmother

Kinuko: Yukiko's elder sister

Masako: Yukiko's younger sister

Takao: Yukiko's younger brother

Sadao: Yukiko's younger brother

Kiyo: nanny

Zeki Bayat: Turkish naval officer and Ertuğrul student to Japan

Hüsrev Gerede: Turkish ambassador to Japan

Mustafa Kemal Atatürk: The first President of the Republic of Turkey

General Jo Iimura: Ryusuke's boss at Imperial Japanese army

Marquis / General Toshinari Maeda: Ryusuke's friend

Koji Okubo: Professor of Turkish studies and the Director for the Institute for Islamic Area Studies

Noel Nouet: French teacher, artist and author

Rüştü Erdelhün: Military attaché to the Turkish embassy in Tokyo

(Japanese names are written in the English order; i.e., given name preceding family name. However, historic names such as feudal lords are written in the Japanese order; i.e., family name preceding given name)

1

The Encounter with Hachiko

On a Sunday morning in May of 1929, Yukiko and Masako were walking to Shibuya Station with their father, Ryusuke Yonezawa. They lived in Shoto, a residential area about 10 minutes walk from Shibuya station, in Tokyo. The road followed a downhill slope through a quiet residential section; passing tasteful houses surrounded by gardens. Some of them were dark brown Japanese houses and others were sophisticated western houses in many different designs such as colonial, French, art deco and many more.

Yukiko was seven; Masako, five. Both were dressed in pretty, flower-print dresses, with a ribbon belt tied in the back. They wore white hats with brims decorated with an aqua blue ribbon for Yukiko and a baby pink ribbon for Masako. In the 1920s, western style clothes had become popular among people in a big city like Tokyo, though most women wore their traditional kimonos.

"I'm so excited–buying a western doll! I'll get one with curly blond hair and blue eyes," Masako said.

"Yes, yes, yes." Yukiko could barely contain herself. "I'll get a French doll with long dark brown hair... dressed in lace. Daddy, do they sell French dolls at Mitsukoshi?" asked Yukiko; looking up at her father.

"The department store sells many things from foreign countries. So they should have dolls from France and America. Italy, China, Germany. You name it," said Ryusuke; smiling at his daughters.

Ryusuke was a military officer and a diplomat. He spoke Chinese, French, and Turkish. He was drawn to western culture and had many foreign friends. Yet, was steeped in the ancient ways. His ancestors were samurai of the Kuroda clan, in Fukuoka, from Kyushu, in the south. Considering that his family had served the lords of Kuroda for nearly 300 years, it was no wonder the samurai blood still coursed through his veins.

In the 1920s, there were quite a few people like Ryusuke in Japan; especially among officers: their love of western culture, modern philosophy, and aesthetics. Yet the inexorable pull of earlier days–in the Edo period (Edo was then the capital) when the shogun ruled, and the world of the samurai flourished for almost three centuries (from 1603 to 1868).

Yukiko and Masako held hands as they neared Shibuya; passing a row of nice shops near the station: a clock shop and a bookstore, a bakery and a stationery store, a French restaurant and several other shops displaying stylish merchandise in glass display cases. Dotted here and there–small two-storied buildings built in western style; their cream-colored walls covered with plaster and accented with arabesque reliefs. The signboards were painted with colorful modern pictures of their products and chic lettering to attract people coming and going. The girls' minds danced and whirled as they contemplated the jumble of words and shapes.

Ahead lies Shibuya station: sophisticated–with its clock tower and huge arched window. Several red streetcars lumber slowly across the plaza, that stands open; inviting people for a stroll. As the station was located in the bottom of the valley, gentle slopes extended in several directions. The roads were equipped with classical street lamps to which egg shaped light bulbs added nostalgic elegance to the scenery. People in kimonos and others in western clothes–pass each other, without noticing. Those in kimonos–flick their parasols. Those in western clothing adjust their hats. The phrase satsukibare (fine May weather) is heard, among the rustling of the leaves. It is a good season to be walking about. A time for light clothing. Many men–both those in kimonos or in western suits–are wearing panama hats, that had become very popular in the 1920s.

Figure 2: Shibuya station circa 1920s.

Presently, the three strollers noticed a big Akita dog pacing up and down, in front of the station. He was mostly white, with long sturdy legs. Yukiko and Masako came up to him. He stood as high as their faces. When they drew close, the dog stopped for a moment and stared at them quietly. One ear was bent, and he had a look of sadness about him; sadness, and a great loneliness. After inspecting the girls, he suddenly turned away and walked to the ticket gate, where he stood gazing into the office.

"Daddy, I wonder who owns this dog. He looks so lost," said Yukiko.

"Wait! He must be Hachiko," Ryusuke answered.

"Hachiko? How come you know his name?"

"He is quite famous. I heard about him from Mrs. Kikkawa, our nice neighbor. She told me that Hachiko was Professor Ueno's dog. You know the beautiful

Japanese house with the policeman's box on the opposite side of the gate?"

"Oh, the house with a black Japanese gate, near our house?"

"Yes. That was professor Ueno's house until four years ago. Hachiko always accompanied professor Ueno when he left in the morning and walked with him to Shibuya station. After seeing him off at the ticket gate, he came home. Then in the evening he returned to the station again, to greet professor Ueno. He was so attached to professor Ueno. But professor Ueno died suddenly at work. Which, of course, Hachiko could not have known. And so the dog has been coming to the station every day, to greet his master. Every day–for the last four years,"

"Oh, poor Hachiko! Every day," Masako repeated sadly.

"He is so loyal!" answered Yukiko, and looked at the dog.

While they were talking, Hachiko settled in on his stomach, with his forepaws extended in from of him; reminding Ryusuke of the sphinx. The whiteness of his coat–stood out from the anonymous passers-by.

Yukiko and Masako thought how wonderful it would be if professor Ueno could suddenly reappear. They could imagine Hachiko's eyes glowing like an evening star; his tail wagging furiously; and the dog actually smiling, as he jumped up and ran to his master. And professor Ueno opening his arms wide and enfolding his faithful friend. The girls had a dog at home, and they well-knew the love an animal could have.

They were jarred from their reverie by Ryusuke, who hurried them inside, and to the counter, where they purchased tickets. They rode several stops to Kanda station; then disembarked and set off on foot, in the direction of Nihonbashi. Nihonbashi: the center of Edo (old Tokyo) until well after the Meiji restoration in the 19th century when the reign of the Edo Shogun ended...and modern Japan began to emerge. Nihonbashi translates as a Japanese bridge. A bridge to where...who can say? This bridge symbolizes Edo (Tokyo), and the distance to the rest of Japan is measured from here now and then. This bridge was officially named as the starting point of the five major roads in 1604. Before railroads were introduced, people in Edo started their long journeys from Nihonbashi. On the other hand, local people traveling from far away places aimed for Nihonbashi as their destination.

Mitsukoshi department store's predecessor was a famous kimono shop 'Echigoya', established in 1673. In 1904, the store announced that they would become an American style emporium, that sold everything from clothes to cosmetics; hats and shoes and umbrellas; medicine, kimonos, and points west. And east. And so in 1914, there appeared, as if by magic, a beautiful five-story Renaissance style building, that became a popular gathering place for people who liked western culture, and... for those who liked kimonos.

The three strolled along Chuo street for about 10 minutes–commenting, pointing, laughing–until they arrived at the entrance of the department store.

"Look! The lion statues that mom told us about!" cried Masako. The two big lions squatting dignifiedly at the entrance... were replicas of London's Trafalgar Square lions. The white stone building was decorated with refined geometric pattern reliefs. The façade was decorated with gold trim and gilded lights. Within, crystal chandeliers hung suspended from the atrium–like a scene from a Renaissance painting. The atmosphere was very once-upon-a-time. Very European.

This was the girls' first time to the department store. Until recently, they were living in Taipei, Taiwan, which at the time, was a colony of Japan. Ryusuke had been posted there by the Japanese government in 1923, and he took his wife, his two daughters (Yukiko, then a baby, and her elder sister, Kinuko), his mother Tei, and a nanny. In Taiwan, Masako and the two boys, Takao and Sadao, were born, so that on their return to Japan in 1929, they had become a family of seven.

Many attractive western buildings built by the Japanese existed in Taiwan. One of the most famous was the Governor-General's office, built in 1895, from white stone accented with red bricks. This was where Ryusuke worked, and his office–in the Baroque-style building with its 60-meter-tall central tower—had become a familiar place for them. Museums, hospitals and universities were housed in western-style buildings... that nestled among the tall tropical betel nut trees. All, indelible memories for the children.

Since their recent return to Tokyo, they settled in Shoto, Shibuya. They had not been to places like Tokyo station or the Ginza district, with its modern edifices. To Yukiko and Masako, everything was new and exciting, right down to the dark gray bronze lions that welcomed all with the curiosity to step through its portals.

Ryusuke led them to a section that sold pretty dolls: from traditional Japanese ichima dolls with black bobbed hair and dressed in kimonos—to imports from France and America, and from wherever dolls are born. Including Lenci dolls from Italy, and others dressed in stylish art-deco costumes. The girls squealed with delight.

"Some are for adults," Ryusuke explained. "They're too expensive for children. Here's one of Rudolf Valentino! The famous Hollywood actor. Your mother would like this one!" he laughed.

"Wow, he looks too real to me. We want pretty girl dolls," said Yukiko.

Their elder sister Kinuko had received a French doll, given to her a few years before, by their uncle—captain of a great ocean liner. At that time, Yukiko and Masako were little, and got diminutive baby dolls. Now they were "grown up," and wanted girl dolls with fancy dresses.

Ryusuke agreed to take them to a department store... for dolls. After an endless array of coiffeurs and apple-cheeked faces, of footwear and apparel, they finally chose two. Yukiko got a 15-inch French doll with gorgeous brown eyes and long ringleted hair. The doll's white lace dress accented with peach satin bows was exactly what Yukiko dreamed of. Masako chose a blond curly hair doll with smiling blue eyes made in America. The doll had a white sailor dress with blue lines and a red scarf. Decorated with a red ribbon on her head, the doll looked so cheerful. Ryusuke told the salesgirl that he would take them. Yukiko and Masako looked at the salesgirl as she wrapped the dolls in special boxes and tied them with a red ribbon. She put them in two separate shopping bags and handed them to the girls. They were delighted.

Ryusuke then took them to a restaurant at the top of the store. They were seated at a table covered with a white linen cloth. The dining chairs upholstered in red velvet and chandeliers hanging from the ceiling made the little girls feel like they were in a palace. Ryusuke had a clear-cut face, high bridged nose and big eyes that are often seen among the people from Kyushu. Wearing a moustache and in a light gray suit, he looked well suited to a westernized restaurant. Yukiko and Masako put their doll packages very carefully on a chair. They kept smiling, thinking of the beautiful dolls they would take home that day.

The restaurant had a special menu featuring 'a child's lunch', a new and very popular item consisting of a Mount-Fuji-shaped cone of rice, finger sandwiches, spaghetti, croquettes, and dessert; all in very small portions nicely arranged on an octagonal plate and decorated with a small Japanese flag. Ryusuke ordered 'a child's lunch' and orange juice for the girls and sandwiches and coffee for himself. After lunch, they went to the ground floor and noticed the salesgirls were distributing alphabet cookies (small cookies shaped in alphabet letters) in small bags to children as a promotion of the store. Receiving small bags, Yukiko and Masako looked at each other with big smiles.

They walked back to Kanda station. The girls were exhilarated, holding the famous shopping bags with pink, blue and dark blue design. The three arrived at Shibuya station around three o'clock. With many people milling about the station. But no sight of Hachiko. They climbed the hill toward home; tired and happy–the girls holding tight to their new possessions.

2

Zeppelin in Shibuya Sky

On the 19th of August in 1929, the world famous German airship LD 127–the Graf Zeppelin– came to Japan, during its round-the-world flight. Before its 4-day stop at the Kasumigaura Naval Air Force Base, it passed across the sky above Tokyo and Yokohama. The news of its coming had been trumpeted in newspapers and broadcast on radio. By the time it arrived, everybody knew about the Graf Zeppelin, and had learned this unfamiliar German word very well.

Ryusuke and the girls sat in the living room, hunched around the radio, listening for news of the approaching giant. The Zeppelin was outfitted with the most modern electronic equipment, and all the messages were broadcast live, with Japanese translations.

"Is the Zeppelin coming soon?" asked Yukiko.

"It should be. Let's get to the slope of Dogenzaka. It's supposed to pass right over Shibuya station," replied Ryusuke with excitement.

"I'll tell Mom and Grandma to hurry up! Then I will tell Takao and Sadao that we'll be leaving soon. Kinu can carry Sadao," said Yukiko, who quickly ran up the stairs.

When she entered Motoko's room, she found her mother and grandmother had just finished putting on their kimonos. Their plan was to go to 'Suiko-sha', the naval officer's club after seeing the Graf Zeppelin in Shibuya, and treat themselves to a western-style dinner there. Suiko-sha was a very sophisticated club; which was why they chose elegant kimonos for the occasion. Takao and Sadao were dressed in the same sailor suits, with short pants and sailor hats. They were told they would see this huge flying ship, and were so excited they began jumping around and flapping their wings. It was all Kiyo could do, to calm them down.

Figure 3: Takao and Sadao in a garden.

Ryusuke was an Army officer but also a member of the Suiko-sha. He thought it would be a good idea to have dinner at the naval officer's club after seeing the airship. His family liked the club and he also hoped to see his friends, who were in charge of the Zeppelin's visit, that fell under the Department of the Navy's supervision.

"Dad told us we should leave in 30 minutes. Is everybody ready?" asked Yukiko.

"We can leave any time. I can't wait to see the Zeppelin. I have to see it with my own eyes, to believe such a huge thing can fly through the air," replied grandmother, Tei.

"Since everyone is ready, we should leave now. We can find a good spot to see the Zeppelin. Kiyo, keep your eyes on Sadao, and if he is tired, please carry him," Motoko said. It was rare for five children to go out together with their parents, but when they did, usually Kinuko, the eldest girl held the hand of Takao, Yukiko held the hand of Masako, the nanny, Kinu stayed close to the youngest, Sadao.

They went to the living room to meet with Ryusuke, Kinuko and Masako.

The three girls were also wearing sailor dresses, which were becoming very popular. Motoko ordered the dresses and suits from the tailor, Madame Ikuma, several months before. For the boys, Motoko decided everything, but for the girls, she let them chose the design and colors they liked. The dresses came out very nice. Their tops were white and the skirts and the lines on the sailor collars were navy for Kinuko, bright green for Yukiko, and orange for Masako. The three girls looked very stylish in their finery–like a cut vase of multi-colored flowers.

They set off down the slope of Dogenzaka, toward Shibuya. The heat had already arrived. Cicadas were chirping in the spruce trees. Mansions of aristocrats and several princes' palaces dotted the hillside and stretched into Shibuya. Surrounded by tall trees, some took on an air of grandeur and mystery, like something precious–hidden away in a forest.

As they approached the station, they could see big crowds gathering in the square, and looking back, knots of people dotting the slopes of Dogenzaka.

In front of a cake shop, a vender was hawking tiny cakes in shape of a Zeppelin, filled with azuki beans or the newly introduced custard cream inside. They were hard to resist–wrapped in beautiful boxes with pictures of the Zeppelin. Needless to say, the children were clamoring for them. And Ryusuke, after casting a wry look at the children, bought one for each.

They slowly retraced their steps up Dogenzaka; the children clutching their new-found booty. Along the slope, people were adjusting their cameras and squinting through binoculars, to catch a glimpse of the approaching behemoth. Radios at shops blared out the messages from the Zeppelin. People were apprehensive, eager. Some, greatly moved. Shouts went up. Fingers pointing skyward. It had come.

"There's the Zeppelin! Look!"

Everyone's eyes fixed on the giant silver cloud descending from the heavens, feeling its way toward Shibuya.

"Wow, it is amazing! "

"Look at the color. Isn't that aluminum? It is so bright!"

"I didn't know it could fly so low. I wonder what it's like, looking down at us through the windows."

People were mesmerized and stared unbelievably at the airship floating by, high above them. As the Zeppelin passed across the sky, it cast its long shadow, so that it felt like a huge cloud hovering over them.

"I never saw such a sight!" Kinuko exclaimed.

"I'm so glad. Masako, aren't we lucky? " said Yukiko.

"Yes! " said Masako. Then, looking back at the station, she remarked: "See! Hachiko is also following the Zeppelin! "

And looking back at the station, they could make out Hachiko–sitting calmly, gazing up at the sky with what seemed like a smile on his face. The scene was perfect: everyone there–people and animals; two-legged and four–all transfixed. All one...in that magic moment.

When the Zeppelin had rejoined its fellow cloud wanderers, Ryusuke turned to everyone and said, "So, are you happy! Shall we go to Suiko-sha and eat curry or something? "

"Yes, let's do that! Kiyo, can you take Takao and Sadao home with you? I think they prefer to go home and have Zeppelin cakes than come to Suiko-sha with us," said Motoko.

Ryusuke, Motoko, Tei and the three girls waved good-by to Kiyo and the boys and walked to the station. They summoned two taxis and headed off to their next adventure. Gastronomic. More down-to-earth. But an adventure, nonetheless.

The gate of Suiko-sha was in a dignified traditional Japanese style. Possibly, the place was a former estate of a feudal lord. The taxis purred through the grand gate and stopped in front of a sophisticated western style building. The club had been used for western manner lessons for the naval officers, formal parties, and lectures. The interior was unmistakably western.

They entered the dining room and were seated at a table. The restaurant served formal French meals as well as popular Japanese dishes such as curry rice, croquettes and hayashi rice (a modified version of hashed beef). The Navy's original curried rice was very popular, and also a favorite of the girls.

While savoring the food, they all talked about the Zeppelin.

"What do you think of the Zeppelin?" Ryusuke asked his mother.

"I was shocked! You know, I was born in the Edo period. My father was still wearing two swords and had a 'chonmage' top-knot when I was little. I never imagined I would see such a sight in my life! " replied Tei.

"Oh, that's right. Masako, do you know when your grandmother was born? " Ryusuke asked the youngest girl, Masako.

"I know. Grandma Tei was born when Commodore Perry came to Japan in the black ships," answered Masako proudly.

"Very good! And what year was that? "

"Well, that was... I forgot!" said Masako looking at Kinuko and Yukiko.

"I learned it at school! That was 1853. Commodore Perry demanded that Shogun, Tokugawa Yoshinobu open the country to the world," replied Yukiko.

"Yes. Grandma was born in a turbulent year in Japanese history," said Ryusuke.

Tei responded thoughtfully: "Of course, I don't remember anything. But when I grew a little older, everyone told me how shocking the incident was! That was when odaiba were built in Tokyo bay" (odaiba were artificial island fortresses built for defensive purpose).

"The ships were called kurobune (the black ships), after their color. Today's airship was silver. But both ships caused a sensation in Japan," said Ryusuke.

"Grandma is amazing! She has lived through so many great periods of history: The Edo, the Meiji periods of, the Taisho era, and the Showa," said Kinuko. Everyone laughed and looked at Tei.

They topped off dinner with ice cream, and left the dining room. Then, they meandered toward the lounge where several men sat drinking and smoking cigars.

Ryusuke stood there and spoke with his wife and mother. "I'll have a drink with my friends here. How about you and the children go for a walk in the garden? "

"That's a good idea. The garden looks pretty, and I would like to walk around after a big dinner," answered Motoko. Then the ladies and the girls went outside to imbibe a bit of nature.

Figure 4: Ryusuke Yonezawa at the Singapore Botanical Gardens.

Ryusuke stepped into a lounge dotted with world globes and ship models. Maps of lands and seas spread across the wood-paneled walls. The bookshelves, intermittently featured glass doors silently guarding rows of books bound in red or blue Moroccan leather. Prussian blue armchairs enclosed mahogany tables. Several men were seated; having drinks and talking to each other. Ryusuke found his cousin, Masataka Ono and came over to him.

"Good evening, Masataka-san."

"Good evening, Ryusuke-san. Glad to see you! Do you know Mr. Yamakawa? " He smiled and looked at the man sitting next to him.

"Excuse me. I don't think so."

"Let me introduce you to Mr. Goro Yamakawa. This is my cousin Ryusuke Yonezawa.

"Very pleased to meet you. Mr. Yonezawa."

The men sat together. Ryusuke ordered a glass of whisky from a waiter; then joined the conversation. Ryusuke was an Army officer and Masataka and Goro from the Naval service. Outside of work, however, men did not address each other by rank.

"So, Masataka-san, are you going to see the Zeppelin at the Kasumigaura Naval Air-Force Base tomorrow? " asked Ryusuke.

"Yes. Actually, it is part of my job. I will have a chance to look at the Zeppelin, including the machine room and the cockpit. The Zeppelin will be shown to the public for four days. It should prove a very popular event. Special trains will be run from Tokyo station, just for the occasion. Lots of people will be there to see the Zeppelin close up."

"The Zeppelin is due to cross the Pacific in a few days, and will finish its round-the-world trip at the Naval Air Station in Lakehurst, New Jersey. It is supposed to be completed in 21 days. Can you believe it?" said Goro.

"So fast. This is becoming the era of speed, isn't it?" said Ryusuke; trying to fit the thought into the context of his own travels.

"By the way, Yonezawa-san, you've been to Tibet and Central Asia. So I've heard," asked Goro.

"Yes. Several years ago. We traveled on horses. It was quite a trip. Cars don't make out very well in that part of the world. There are no roads, no stations for gasoline," answered Ryusuke.

"I've heard you are an excellent horseman. So you must have enjoyed it?" asked Masataka.

Ryusuke loved horseback riding so much that while was living in Taiwan, he intentionally found lodgings far from the Governor-General's Office so he could commute to work by horse, not by foot, as the other officers did. His superior considered it impertinent, and there was some conflict over it.

"Yes, it was interesting. I actually enjoyed it," said Ryusuke. "But I was no match for the Tibetan monks we met in the mountains. The monks offered to buy our horses. The ones we sold them were the hardest to ride. But they mastered them easily; even in their long robes, and galloped away on a steep and narrow mountain road. We were surprised," replied Ryusuke with a smile.

"Speaking of horseback riding, do you know army cavalry lieutenant Takeichi Nishi ?" asked Goro.

"Oh, Baron Nishi? Yes, of course. We get on well," he said (in Japanese, to "get on well" means "get along well with the horse") and continued with a laugh.

"He is an incredible rider and also a great fellow. We rode together in the Setagaya cavalry division. He is going to represent Japan in the 1932 Los Angeles Olympics, for equestrian jumping. With his technique in handling reins, he could easily gallop across a mountain in Tibet," said Ryusuke.

"In an area like that, you need to travel as the ancients did. However, traveling long distance will be much faster than ever, with technology like airships and airplanes," said Goro.

"That's right. Nowadays, people have made records on around-the-world travel by airplanes in 30 days. It is incredible progress," answered Masataka.

The conversation continued, on the quickening pace of the world, and where it might lead. About the old world and the new. And how Japan fitted into the scheme of things. Presently, Ryusuke glanced at his watch, and excused himself; explaining it was time to fetch his family in the garden, and to squire them home.

Masataka and Goro stood up to say good-bye. Ryu-suke went out to the Japanese garden, just as Mo-toko, Tei, and the girls were crossing the bridge on a pond and returning to the building.

"Did you have a nice time?" Ryusuke asked them.

"Ah, yes. It was such a beautiful evening. The garden looked so pretty with stone and paper lanterns all lit up. How about you?" answered Motoko.

"It was good—talking with my cousin Masataka and Mr. Yamakawa. We could've gone on all night, but it is getting late. Time to go home," Ryusuke add-ed. They walked to the entrance to catch a taxi. The cars glided silently through the gate and out into the night.

3

Grandmother & Old Tales

*I*t was an early morning in April, 1930. At that time, Kinuko, Yukiko, and Masako all went to Omukai elementary school, which was a 10 minute walk from their house. Takao and Sadao attended kindergarten nearby.

The children were sitting at the dining room table with Ryusuke and Motoko, eating oatmeal and drinking milk. Oatmeal was still new in Japan, though people who liked the western life style started having it for breakfast, as it was said to be very nutritious. For the same reason, people encouraged their children to drink milk. The Olympic gold medalist swimmer, Johnny Weissmuller (aka Tarzan) also became very popular in Japan. The Japanese people learned that his mother encouraged Johnny, who was a weak boy, to take swimming lessons and drink lots of milk. Modern parents followed the example and started to send their children to swimming classes and encouraged them to drink milk. The Yonezawa family was no exception.

"Mom, is this Napoleon?" asked Yukiko while examining the face of the Quaker man on the box of oatmeal. Beaming out from the red and blue box was the famous trademark of the Quaker man smiling in his navy blue hat.

"What?" said Motoko, who looked at Ryusuke and then they burst into laughter.

"Yukiko, this is a Quaker, a religious group in America. The company chose the portrait of the man for his gentle happy nature. Not quite like Napoleon!"

"Oh, I thought the hat looked like Napoleon's. I always thought we've been eating Napoleon oatmeal!"

"Me, too. I thought this was a French breakfast," said Masako. And the girls started laughing.

They were eating oatmeal with Sun-Maid raisins. The children were drinking milk and the adults were drinking English tea. They could buy these imported products at the Meiji-ya store in Ginza. Ryusuke also bought cheese and liked to eat it with wine. The other family members weren't quite ready for cheese.

While they were eating, grandmother Tei came back. She had gone for her morning walk in the neighborhood.

"Welcome back, mother," said Motoko.

"Good morning, grandmother," said all the children.

"Good morning everyone. Oh, dear, I nearly fell on the slope, on the way to Shibuya station! Someone threw a banana peel on the road. I slipped on it. I could barely grab on to a bamboo fence near by. What bad manners to throw a banana skin," Tei said, in an angry voice.

"Are you all right? It was good you were not hurt. It would be awful if you broke your bones," said Ryu-suke.

"Don't worry. I am fine!" Tei answered. And she sat down with the family.

The children looked at each other with a little mischievous smile, imagining their grandmother slipping on a banana peel. Tei was a strong, funny, and very savvy grandmother. And they loved her very much.

"Mother, would you like to have oatmeal and tea, or rice and miso soup?" asked Motoko.

"Well, I'll have a Japanese breakfast. Rice, miso soup, seaweed and an egg will be good. Setsu, could you bring it for me?" she asked to the maid.

Tei sat down with everyone. She was in her 70s, but looked young, with a straight back and short hair. In those days old ladies wore kimonos, their hair piled on top of their heads. Tei also wore a kimono, but she had her silver hair cut very short and slicked down in back with camellia oil. She was slim, tall and walked very quickly. It was her custom to go for a walk around town before breakfast.

"I went to Shibuya station and noticed Hachiko there. He was already sitting by the ticket gate...waiting. Oh, he is a beautiful Akita. The saleswoman at the newspaper stand told me more things about him. She mentioned that after professor Ueno suddenly died about five years ago, Mrs. Ueno had to move from the big house in Shibuya to a smaller place in Setagaya (a district next to Shibuya). She tried to keep Hachiko in the new house. But Hachiko resisted being chained up. Mrs. Ueno tried very hard, but finally gave up and released him.

Since then, Hachiko came back to Shibuya station and never returned to the house in Setagaya. Mrs. Ueno understood that Hachiko missed professor Ueno and Shibuya so much. So she asked their former gardener, Kikusaburo Kobayashi, who lived near Shibuya station, to keep Hachiko. He agreed. From then on, Hachiko has resumed his former rounds: traveling to Shibuya station in mornings and evenings from the gardener's house. It's been nearly five years...and he has never missed a day! Such a loyal dog! It made me cry," Tei told everyone.

"That's so sad. He has been waiting for a master who will never come back?" Kinuko asked.

"Yes! On rainy days, snowy days, and windy days. He has never missed a single one," Tei answered, brushing a tear from her eye.

"I heard that Akita dogs will have only one master. That was why they were so highly prized by samurai lords during the Middle Ages," said Ryusuke.

Takao, who had been focusing on eating his oatmeal, stopped eating and asked Ryusuke: "What did you say? Akita dogs are samurai? "

"Oh, I said samurai treasured Akita dogs. But I guess they are a form of samurai, since they are so loyal to their masters," Ryusuke said and smiled to the little boy.

"So, Hachiko is a samurai dog," Takao said with a serious face.

"Well, everyone, it is time to go to school. It is 7:30 A.M," said Ryusuke.

"Grandmother, can you tell us an old story tonight? " Yukiko asked.

"Sure. Do you want to listen to the rest of the 'Ghost Cat of Nabeshima' ? asked Tei, looking at the girls.

"Wow, that was so spooky. Maybe that, or...something else." Answered Masako.

"I will. I'll tell you a very interesting old story tonight. But right now you better hurry up. Don't be late for school," answered Tei.

The children said good-by to the parents and grandmother and then left for school. The nanny Kiyo was waiting for the boys and walked with them to kindergarten. It became quiet after the children left.

***

"Will you go to the Tokyo University of Foreign Studies today?" Motoko asked Ryusuke. He was teaching at the university a couple of times a week.

"Yes, so I can leave home at 8:30 A.M. today," he said.

Tei was having a cup of tea after her Japanese breakfast and chatted with them.

"I heard a bit about why Hachiko couldn't keep living at professor Ueno's house. It wasn't known to the public, but professor Ueno and Yaeko-san were not married," said Tei.

"Oh, really?" answered Motoko. Tei continued.

"Professor Ueno was supposed to marry a woman from a prominent family; it was arranged by both families. But professor Ueno and Yaeko loved each other and they promised to get married. But neither family approved. And so they lived together, and people called Yaeko 'Mrs. Ueno'. But professor Ueno died unexpectedly and Yaeko had no legal rights to the house. She was forced to move, and stayed at an acquaintance's house for a while. Yet, it was impossible to keep a big dog like Hachiko, and she asked her relatives to keep him. Of course, it was very difficult for them, as Hachiko didn't take to strangers," Tei explained, as she paused to sip her tea.

"I've heard Akitas are the most difficult of dogs," offered Motoko.

"That's right. They are gentle with their owners, but aloof from strangers. But then a nice thing happened. Professor Ueno's students admired their teacher greatly; they looked upon him as a father, many such students. They felt sorry for Yaeko and Hachiko's situation. So they collected money and bought a house in Setagaya for her and Hachiko," said Tei.

"Such a gesture. To present a house to their professor's widow! They were loyal to their teacher, just as Hachiko was–to his master!" Ryusuke said thoughtfully.

"Mother, you have always been so good at collecting such stories," Ryusuke said, appreciatively.

"That was why she was called by the lord of Kuroda to tell him the stories of the streets when she was living at the castle," said Motoko smiling.

Tei was a daughter of Shinpachiro Miyamura, a samurai of the Kuroda clan during the Edo period. Shinpachiro was in charge of guarding the Ooku (section of the castle where the women connected to the reigning lord resided. Only the lord and a few men were allowed entry into in this section).

As Shinpachiro was close to the lord because of his job, Tei often had chances to see the lord when she was little. The lord found that Tei was very smart and quick-witted so he invited her to study with his daughter, the princess of Kuroda. In that way, Tei got to study Japanese classics, Japanese short poems, Confucianism, mathematics, proper etiquette, court language, and many other things. It was so very fortunate for Tei, as girls in general in those days weren't afforded the opportunity of much learning.

The lord of Kuroda enjoyed listening to Tei's stories of the streets. Since he was not free to walk about unnoticed, he was eager to learn about quotidian life beyond the castle walls. He often said "Call Tei here. I want to hear the stories of the streets," and she would be invited to his room where the lord and a few important ladies were seated, and recite to them tales of the every day—the mundane and the miraculous.

In this way, Tei improved her ability to collect interesting stories and became a good talker and a good listener.

While she was living at the castle, she was given dolls and books from the princess—gifts she cherished for more than 60 years. She kept them in boxes called tsuzura (durable and light traditional bamboo boxes coated with lacquer) in a closet of her room.

They finished drinking tea and Ryusuke left for a work.

***

The boys returned before lunch, and the house began to bubble once again. They loved to ride on tricycles in the yard and do sumo wrestling. Several foreign students from Asia were also staying at the house.

They were very kind and played sumo wrestling with them. The boys loved this.

In the afternoon, the girls came back from Omukai elementary school. On the way to and from the school, they passed by professor Ueno's house. After hearing the story from Tei, they stopped in front of it. Someone else was living there now, but otherwise, nothing had changed since Hachiko's time.

It was a big traditional Japanese house surrounded by a wooden fence. The front gate with a black roof and double gate folding black doors stood open. Opposite the gate was a policeman's box, with an officer on duty. The girls bowed to the policeman and tarried for a few minutes. The policeman nodded with a smile.

Within, a garden path with several trees on the left, flanking large flat stones leading to the main entrance. On the right: a low bamboo fence with another gate leading to a bigger Japanese garden. This contained a 'chashitsu'–a traditional Japanese tea room. The girls imagined Hachiko coming out the black gate with professor Ueno. They wondered how the professor and Hachiko communicated. With looks, with words, with woofs. They wondered what they said. Or if they just knew. Knew all they needed to...about what was in each others' hearts. Then they left, and began the climb up the gentle slope, to home.

***

At the dinner table, Yukiko told everyone that they looked at Hachiko's house and noticed the beautiful Japanese tea room.

"I heard Mrs. Ueno was a tea ceremony master and was giving lessons," Tei added.

"Those students who gave her a house in Setagaya also built a tea room for her. I was so glad to hear that the students were so nice to her."

Professor Ueno had studied in Europe and America when he was young.

At that time, quite a few people preferred to live a western lifestyle after they returned from Europe or America. However, it seems professor Ueno liked the traditional Japanese lifestyle. He was living in a typical Japanese house, had a traditional tea room, and kept an Akita dog.

According to his students, when they gathered in a Japanese room at his house for study sessions, Hachiko always joined them. On the occasion of a cherry blossom viewing party, Hachiko, who was still a puppy at the time, was given a bath before the party and sat on professor Ueno's lap in a Japanese room and enjoyed the cherry blossom viewing with the guests. He was allowed in the Japanese tatami mat rooms all the time.

Figure 5: Grandmother Tei's old books of otogizoushi.

After dinner, Tei invited the children for a story. Tei's room was a traditional Japanese room on the ground floor, looking out on to a pond. It was a beautiful evening and the half moon was riding clear in the cloudless sky. The garden lay dark and heavily-wooded. The moon tipped the branches silver, casting leaf shadows on the ground. The evening was still as a picture.

Tei took out several otogizoushi (old fairy tale) books from her tsuzura (a traditional bamboo box coated with lacquer), and lay them on the tatami floor. These old books were fashioned from wood block impressed on Japanese rice paper. Colorful illustrations adorned the jackets and overflowed the pages: a vast array of characters, including princesses and samurai; actors, ghosts, animals and scenes of nature; even several scientific drawings, like a hot air balloon. The girls loved the pictures. But alas, the books—written in an old cursive style—were completely unintelligible to them.

Tei had been an instructor of Tokiwazu—a style of music and singing used in the kabuki theater for dance and dance plays. She was gifted with a strong voice, and over the years, had grown artful at telling stories.

"Let's see: what shall we read tonight? Do you want to hear what happened to the 'Ghost Cat of Nabeshima' ?" she asked.

"No, please," whispered Masako. "I was so scared I had to ask Yukiko to go to the bathroom with me, and wait outside."

"Yes, Masako said the hallway was too scary to walk down, so I had to hold hands with her to go there. Not again tonight," added Yukiko.

"All right. So I will read 'The Tale of Shiranui'. This is a great fantasy of Princess Wakana. How about that?" asked Tei.

"Oh, that will be fun. Princess Wakana has supernatural power, right?" answered Kinuko,who had heard part of the story before.

"Yes, you are right. Princess Wakana was a daughter of the 16th century Christian lord of Kyushu, Otomo Sourin. The story is a fantasy of her revenge against her father's enemies, using her magical power. Shall I read the book?" asked Tei. The children agreed.

Then Tei began to read, She was so good at modulating her voice to accommodate the characters: the highs, the lows, the women and the men, even the sounds of animals.

The children listened, entranced; imagining the scenes in their heads. The faint light that Tei left on–bathed the room in shadows. Otherwise, all was dark. The rest of the room was pitch dark. In this atmosphere, the children were transported to the magical world of medieval Japan. Outside, the house was very quiet. The only noise to be heard was the sound of wooden clappers, by a night watchman, who called out: "hi no youjin" (make sure to put your fire out). The old phrase–endlessly repeated–and the echoes of watchman's wooden blocks–carried the children back across the centuries.

Yukiko's House and Frequent Meeting with Hachiko

At the end of 1930, Ryusuke's family moved from Shibuya, to the neighboring Setagaya district, which was only 2 stops from Shibuya station by streetcar. When Ryusuke's family returned to Tokyo from Taipei, they could have lived at their old house in Bunkyo district, in central Tokyo. This was a traditional Japanese house he inherited from his ancestors. The neighborhood had the charm of old Edo. But the tenant he rented the house to when he was transferred to Taiwan–wished to stay. And Ryusuke was interested in living in a suburban area, such as Shibuya and Setagaya, which were popular at the time.

The avant garde had begun to build western-style houses in the suburbs and adopt a modern life style.

He started to look for a home there, as well, and first rented one in Shibuya. Their place was only several houses away from professor Ueno's. The name of the town was Shoto, which once belonged to Marquis Nabeshima (the descendant of lord of the Nabeshima clan), who used it as a farm and a tea estate. Part of the estate was sold for residences. People built sophisticated houses, and the area became popular among intellectual types such as writers, professors, and military officers. Ryusuke, who liked modern and stylish things, decided to continue renting his house in central Bunkyo, and moved to Shoto. After a year or so, Ryusuke found a nice one formerly owned by a doctor in Setagaya. As the house was used for the doctor's clinic and the family's residence, it was very spacious and perfect for a large family. He bought this house and the family moved to Setagaya. He also liked the location because it was close to the Setagaya Cavalry Regiment.

Ryusuke and Motoko decided to continue sending the girls to Omukai elementary school from Setagaya. The boys enrolled in a kindergarten near by. So the girls began riding a streetcar to Shibuya station every day, for school. They got off at Shibuya and walked the slope to the school. Kinuko had a music lesson at school in the morning, and being 10 years old, she was big enough to commute by herself. Yukiko and Masako were told to go to school and come home together. It was a custom for them to do many things together, so that Masako would always follow wherever Yukiko went. It was quite an adventure for two little girls–traveling to school by streetcar. Something they were proud of.

More often now, they would see Hachiko at Shibuya station. He was not there when they returned, as it was too early for the dog to take up his post. But there he was every morning, sitting quietly and earnestly, in front of the ticket gate. After a month passed, they began to pat him. Yukiko knew that by this time Hachiko must have recognized them.

"Masako, let's pat Hachiko today," Yukiko said.

"Do you think it's ok? He won't bite me?" Masako asked.

"He's a gentle dog. It's ok. Pat him very softly," Yukiko said, approaching the dog and patting his neck. Hachiko started to wag his tail, opened his mouth and showed a happy expression.

"See, he likes it. He knows us," Yukiko said, and smiled at Hachiko. Masako approached cautiously, and rubbed him gently on the head.

"Hachiko, you are a good dog," Masako said, grinning. With such attention being lavished on him, Hachiko began to squirm with joy, and they could feel the warmth and affection emanating from him.

"His fur is coarse outside, but it is very soft inside, isn't is?" Yukiko asked.

"Yes, it is so thick," Masako said and combed down his back. Several people were passing by and smiled when they noticed the girls patting Hachiko. After several minutes, they suddenly realized they would be late, and hurried off to school.

"Masako, we have to run. Let's go now. Good-by, Hachiko," Yukiko said and pulled her hand away.

"Bye-bye, Hachiko, see you tomorrow morning," Masako said and off they ran towards the slope.

After that, the bond was sealed, and it became their custom to pat him whenever they had a chance.

Figure 6: The mezzanine floor and a dog house in Yukiko's house.

Yukiko's new house in Setagaya was traditional Japanese, with western influence. An architectural firm 'America-ya', established by a man who had studied in America, designed it. 'America-ya's houses were built with all elements imported from America, including building materials, windows, doors, and fireplaces. In the 1920s people started to build many western style houses. 'America-ya' houses were not of completely western design. But rather a blend of Japanese and western style and favored by people who liked western culture.

There were over 200 'America-ya' houses in Tokyo and Yukiko's house was one of them.

It was several steps up, to the gate, as the house was on slope. Because of the incline, a small hill rose up behind the pond and the garden that surrounded it. But while the house looked Japanesy from the outside, it proved very eclectic within.

The entrance hall opened out onto a western style living room. The floor was of green and white checker, patterned linoleum; material recently introduced to Japan. In the wall: a bay window with blinds. The gas heater, with doors of white mica, looked warm and inviting. An art-deco style chandelier hung from the ceiling and lit the room with a rich yellow glow.

In the center stood a massive table hewed from the center slice of a Taiwanese cypress. Around the table: chairs and a sofa upholstered in caramel-colored velvet and covered with white lace. On the wall, an oil painting of Istanbul in a gold frame with complicated relief. The phantasmagoria of mosques and palaces against the Bosporus—incarnated the currents of the times: the brave new world of Atatürk; the uneasy seductions of western civilization.

Several small gold statues of a Tibetan Buddha–peered out from a black lacquered cabinet. Ryusuke brought these back from Tibet. They were treasured.

And always received an offering of candles and flowers. A selection of Asian masks hung from the wall; some brought back by Ryusuke; others, gifts from the Asian people who had stayed at their house.

A modern item in the room was a phonograph. It was nicely stored in a square wooden box, and when they listened to music, they opened the lid.

First, you put a record on the turntable; you then cranked the handle for a long time. As it began to turn, one carefully placed a chrome handle with a needle–on the record. You could listen for a while... until the turntable gradually slowed, and the sound become strange. To restore it, you would have to crank the handle more. A record case covered with lavender color silk offered many records from Japanese popular songs of the times, and classic music such as Mozart, Beethoven, Bach, Schubert and so on. Among the family's favorites were the aria of the opera "Mignon" by Amboise Thomas, "Le Cygne" (Swan) of "Le Carnaval des Animaux" by Saint-Saens, and "Humoresque" by Dvorak. Plus records from RCA Victor with their burgundy-colored labels featuring another famous dog: the Victor trademark of 'His Master's Voice.'

Several tropical plants–a small palm tree, bougainvillea, and orchids–called from the alcoves. Ryusuke had become interested in tropical plants, especially orchids, while was living in Taiwan.

Except for the living room and kitchen, the other rooms were in Japanese style. People removed their shoes when entering the house (an ancient custom), so that the hall contained a place for leaving footwear; replete with shoehorn.

The Japanese rooms were either used in the traditional Japanese way, which meant no furniture was placed on the tatami mat floor, or in the modified western way, with the tatami covered by carpeting. The traditional Japanese rooms had basically no furniture except for a low wooden table. People sat on cushions, and slept on futons, that were stored in a closet during the daytime.

In those days, it was common for tatami rooms to have corridors made of wood. Which afforded far more usable space, as people could also place furniture in the corridor instead of the tatami room.

In Ryusuke's study, a carpeted tatami room, was a big desk and chair. This was where he worked: preparing speeches, translating documents for the army, and working on his book.

Including two helpers, Kiyo and Setsu, and Ryusuke's mother, Tei, there were 10 people normally living in the house at any one time. On top of that, Ryusuke invited Asian students from Thailand, Burma, India and other parts of south-east Asia, to lodge there. Usually, there were around 10 students living with them in the house. He also often invited Turkish and French friends to their house. Sometimes, a son of a mining king from Kyushu visited Tokyo with his servant, to study Tokyo life style (or just to have fun) and stayed at their house. Ryusuke's ancestors were from Kyushu and he loved to entertain these friends from his old home.

These guests from all over the world stayed on the mezzanine. There were seven steps near the entrance hall to a mezzanine, which contained two big rooms covered with tatami mats. The two tatami rooms could be opened up to a large single room because the rooms were separated by traditional sliding doors called shoji. Putting the number of the guests' futons on the tatami floor, they hosted many students and guests in this mezzanine. Another stairway led to the second floor, for the family. The arrangement allowed privacy for family and guests.

In front of the mezzanine room was a green paulownia tree with thick bright green leaves. The mezzanine was a place for guests, but also a wonderful play area for the children. The Asian students were very kind and funny. They welcomed the children to come to the mezzanine and play with them.

In the early Showa era, many Asian leaders felt they could learn from Japan, to be independent and modernize their own countries. And so many students were sent there, to study Japanese and Japanese institutions. Many learned to speak the language well. Also, Ryusuke taught French and Turkish to his children, and some of the students spoke French fluently; thus, allowing the children the opportunity of communicating with them in a European language.

The long wide corridor was like a stage, and Kinuko, Yukiko, Masako and sometimes Takao and Sadao played charades—a very popular game among children, at the time. For this, you needed nothing but some acting and some imagination. The Asian students often joined the game and made them laugh with funny answers.

Underneath the mezzanine floor was an open space with a large dog house. There, they kept a Mongolian dog named 'Aka' (red). Ryusuke had traveled to China, Tibet, Mongolia, and other Asian countries. Several years before, he brought back two Mongolian puppies. He was asked by Marquis Maeda to bring a famous Mongolian dog from the continent. He gave one to the Marquis and kept the other one for himself. They took the puppy to Taiwan and brought him back with them. Now the dog lived at their house in Setagaya. Mongolian dogs were huge Siberian dogs with long thick fur. The one that Ryusuke kept was reddish brown. Which was why they named him 'Aka'. He had a big head with a lion-like mane and looked very scary. Aka was actually well-trained and quite friendly. Ryusuke or one of the house-guest students was in charge of taking Aka for a walk. Even the neighbors enjoyed looking at this giant, gentle creature.

A typical Japanese garden adorned the property: a pond, a small hill, a wisteria trellis, and several stone lanterns. The garden was large and filled with many kinds of trees. Then, there was a wild red pine: it appeared to be painted on the backdrop of a Kabuki theater. An evergreen of pine needles with curvy bonsai–like branches–added a poetic atmosphere to the garden.

Figure 7: At Yukiko's house circa 1931, from the front row left, Takao, right, Masko, back row left, Motoko and right, Yukiko.

"Come outside, everyone!" Ryusuke called to the children from the Garden. Motoko was standing by the wisteria trellis admiring the light purple flowers cascading from the frame. She was wearing a light gray striped pattern kimono with a mauve obi. Her hair was nicely tied on top of her head and secured with an art–deco-design–green and black hair comb. She liked to dress her children in western clothes, but preferred to wear a kimono most of the time.

"Mom, you look pretty under the wisteria trellis!" shouted Kinuko from the Japanese room in front of the pond.

"Yes, she does! Call Yukiko, Masako, Takao and Sadao. I will take a family portrait in the garden. Today is a perfect day for pictures."

While Kinuko was searching for the children in the house, Ryusuke prepared the Zeiss camera he had recently bought. He always brought a camera with him whenever he traveled and was very good at snapping pictures. In their house were many albums with the photos he took in foreign countries–scenes from Tibet and China; Mongolia and Cambodia; Burma, Thailand, and Central Asia.

Ryusuke told Kinuko to call his mother, Tei and nanny, Kinu and maid Setsu as well. Everyone changed to nice dresses and came out to the garden. It was a special thing to take the family portrait at that time. At first, Ryusuke told his wife Motoko and the three girls to stand under the wisteria trellis and took a picture. Then he told the boys and Tei to join the picture. He tried to take pictures in several different combinations in different places.

When the session was over, they all sat on the 'engawa' (the wooden flooring extension facing the garden) and asked Setsu to bring tea and biscuits. It was so nice and cozy–sitting on the engawa on bright sunny days. They admired the beautiful wisteria trellis. Behind it was a tall post with 'koinobori': carp-shaped wind socks decorated for boys' day, which was May 5th. Seven carp (people decorate the number of the family member) with many colors such as black, red, blue, green and orange were flying against the clear blue sky in May. It looked so beautiful and cheerful. As if it would never end.

5

Noel Nouet & Foreigners in Tokyo

Ueno is a huge park that houses a lotus pond, museums, concert halls, and the Tokyo National University of Fine Arts and Music. At first glance, the park looks European, though if you walk around, you will find old Japanese architecture such as the Tosho-gu shrine (the shrine for the Tokugawa shogun family, the ruler of the Edo period), a five storied pagoda, and a temple dedicated to Kannon (the goddess of mercy).

On an island in the lotus pond stands a temple of Benten—the goddess of art and music. The goddess invites you to cross the bridge leading her temple, and receive her benedictions. The park has been a popular place for Japanese as well as foreigners, and has not changed much over the years.

On a Sunday morning in 1932, Ryusuke, Motoko and the three girls were waiting at the entrance of the museum, for a French artist and teacher, Noel Nouet. Mr. Nouet was a good friend of Ryusuke and had been invited by the Ministry of Foreign Affairs in 1926, to teach French at a prestigious high school and the Military Academy. He was attracted by the charm of Japan and the arts and decided to stay in Tokyo. Since then, he had been teaching French at Tokyo Imperial University and the Tokyo University of Foreign Studies. He was also a poet, a writer, and an artist.

This day, they came to see his drawings of Tokyo, that were exhibited at one of the museum's galleries. Noel often came to their house, and had given them several nice sketches of Tokyo scenes. He also sent them post cards with quick sketches drawn on them, from his travels. The Yonezawas loved his drawings and framed and displayed them in the living room. Noel did not speak Japanese; and so they always spoke in French.

Waiting in front of the museum, they noticed Nouet was walking by a fountain and coming to the museum. The girls addressed him: "Bonjour, professeur Nouet," and walked toward him, smiling. They liked Noel. He also sometimes gave them movie tickets to French movies at La Maison Franco-Japonaise; such films were quite special in those days in Japan. Noel answered the girls warmly, and then greeted Ryusuke and Motoko in French. At that time, there were quite a few people who spoke French in Japan.

French was a popular language and French words such as café, savon, metro, parfait, etc. were used like Japanese words back then.

"Bonjour, Nouet-san, we are looking forward to seeing your 'Scenes of Tokyo' exhibition," said Ryusuke.

Noel had been making drawings of many famous places in Tokyo. His beautiful sketches appeared in magazines and newspapers. He had gained a good reputation and was now having an exhibition.

The Yonezawas entered the gallery and began to study the works. Several people there came to talk to Noel. The places that he drew were well-known to Japanese people, though with his artistic style, they looked very poetic and left an impression of elegance. For example, the moat of old Edo castle (now the imperial palace) with its cherry blossoms, in the misty rain, and the red shrine standing in Inokashira pond under the shining moon. These were familiar places. Now all had taken on a romantic European quality to them.

After the exhibition, Ryusuke suggested lunch at Seiyo-ken restaurant, by the pond. Seiyo-ken was one of the oldest French restaurants in Japan, and frequented by famous authors and artists. The Edwardian style building–opening on to the pond– was surrounded by many trees.

In the 17th century, a large sitting Buddha housed in a nearby grove–lent an air of mystery to the place. But the Great Earthquake of 1923 toppled the

Buddha's head. And all that remains was the head, mounted on a pedestal. Until that time, Seiyo-ken was famous the world over, for the fusion of the two: the immortal cuisine of the restaurant, and the immortal teaching of the Buddha of Ueno.

They sat at a table on the terrace. But while the restaurant was famous for its elegant repast, its hayashi-rice was also very popular. Ryusuke ordered wine for Noel and himself. Other people ordered Mitsuya cider and everyone ordered hayashi-rice.

After eating lunch, the girls drifted out in the garden and played on a swing set, as they always did. Ryusuke, Noel, and Motoko sat at the table, chatting.

"Nouet-san, are you going to publish a book of your drawings?" asked Motoko.

"Just between us," he replied, "I am planning to make woodblock prints of my 'Scenes of Tokyo' series. A famous woodblock print maker asked me if I was interested. And of course, I could not say no."

"That would be wonderful. I'm sure they'd be stunning as woodblocks," said Ryusuke.

"It will take some time. Right now, we are trying to figure out how to make prints look like detailed drawings by pen," answered Noel.

"Good for you, Nouet-san. I'm sure people will like them," said Motoko.

"How did you become interested in Japanese woodblock prints? " asked Ryusuke.

"My mother had a woodblock print collection of Hiroshige, inherited from the first French Ambassador to Japan who lived in Edo in the 1860s. Growing up looking at these prints got me interested in Japan and Japanese woodblock prints. I'm so excited to be doing this project," answered Noel.

Woodblock printmaking is a very traditional Japanese art and requires the collaboration of several craftsmen. However, there were several foreigners who studied and created woodblock prints before 1900. Emil Orlik of the Austro-Hungarian Empire, Helen Hyde of the US, and Elizabeth Keith of Scotland were early foreign woodblock print artists.

Some years later, in 1936, Noel published a very artistic and charming woodblock print series called 'Scenes of Tokyo, Twenty-Four Views'.

Figure 8: Lunch at Seiyoken in Ueno. Yukiko (right) and Kinuko.

After lunch, they strolled by Shinobazu pond. Ryusuke and Noel talked about the foreigners living in Tokyo. From 1910 on, many had come to live in Japan. Some were sent by their governments, some came on businesses, some were teachers, some were artists, some were missionaries, and some–political refugees. They lived in the big port city of Kobe or the lively capital, Tokyo. About that time, the Japanese people began to enthusiastically adopt western culture. For that reason, there were many ways for foreigners to start a business in Japan. For teachers, artists and musicians, it was easy to make a living by teaching languages, piano, violin, ballet, and other western arts.

The political refugees were mainly those who fled from Russia after the revolution. They were Russians, Tatars, Jews, Poles, and Ukrainians. There was a hotel run by an Armenian family in Kobe, which was a gathering place for those refugees. Many of them had made their living by selling western fabrics, which were much in demand in large cities. Some of them established successful European confectionery companies. An interesting example was an Indian refugee who fled from colonial India and opened a successful curry restaurant in Tokyo.

Then there were the globetrotters, who came to Japan and visited famous places, like Tokyo and Kyoto, Hakone (a view of Mt.Fuji), Nikko (the gorgeous shrine of the first Tokugawa shogun), and Kamakura (the Great Buddha). With all these people from so many parts of the world, Tokyo became an international city.

"It's an exciting time to be living in Tokyo, isn't it?" said Ryusuke.

"Yes, it is. I like the atmosphere from the old Edo period, that still exists in many places. But I love the international circle here. I meet more foreigners in Japan than in France," answered Noel.

"Oh, "Really? "

"Yes. For example, while I was climbing Mt. Fuji, I met a Danish doctor. He spoke French, and we had nice conversation on top of the mountain."

"Yes, French culture is everywhere," Ryusuke said appreciatively.

"And even more. We found something unusual on the ground. It looked like a man-made object. I picked it up and examined it. Surprisingly, it was an old coin from the Shogun Iemitsu's period!"

"That was the first half of the 17th century!"

"It was a very special moment for me. Reflect on it, mon ami: a Dane and a Frenchman coming upon a 17th century coin on top of Mt. Fuji, in the 20th century. I brought it back and have treasured it ever since."

"I wonder who dropped it there? A samurai. Perhaps a pilgrim or a merchant. " Ryusuke said thoughtfully.

"Yes, it is fun to imagine, isn't it? " Noel replied with a smile.

Noel and Ryusuke continued their conversation as they passed the pond. Motoko and the girls followed them, strolling and chatting. Finally, they came to a fork in the road. Noel needed to return to the gallery. The Yonezawas said good-by to him and headed off toward Ueno station.

Mansions in Tokyo

efore the war, there were many beautiful European style mansions in Japan. At that time, a class system existed, and princely families and aristocrats were living in luxurious mansions on vast properties, like the nobility in England. Wealthy commoners also built sophisticated western houses. At the time, these people built a traditional Japanese house and a western house on the same property so they could choose a residence according to whim and occasion. If they preferred to indulge in a bit of western life style, they spent time in the western-style home and used the Japanese house for guests or special ceremonial occasions. If the family preferred a traditional Japanese lifestyle, they dwelled in the Japanese house and used the western house for foreign guests or entertaining.

Figure 9: Marquis Maeda's mansion in Meguro-ku, now a museum.

On a clear autumn day of 1932, Ryusuke, Motoko and the girls, Yukiko and Masako visited Marquis Maeda's mansion in Meguro district, with their Mongolian dog Aka. Meguro is situated next to Setagaya and the Marquis Maeda's estate bordered all three: Shibuya, Meguro, and Setagaya. The family decided to walk to Marquis Maeda's residence—a nice 40-minute walk in a beautiful rural district.

Ryusuke was friends with Marquis Maeda, and they often met each other at military clubs and special events. Today, the family was invited to his recently built residence. Marquis Maeda spent a long time in England as a military officer attached to the embassy in London, and he built an English Tudor style mansion and a traditional Japanese house in Komaba, Meguro in 1930. The western house was considered the most luxurious western style house in the orient.

Ryusuke decided to take his dog Aka to meet Marquis Maeda's dog Kuro, as they were brothers. When Ryusuke traveled to Mongolia, he was asked by Marquis Maeda to bring back Mongolian puppies, that were highly prized in Japan. Ryusuke bought two puppies, a red one and a black one, that were siblings. Marquis Maeda's puppy was black and therefore he named him 'Kuro' (black). It was a special visit for the Yonezawas because the dogs were united again!

Marquis Maeda and Ryusuke shared several interests. They were both military officers, fond of western culture, respected traditional Japanese culture, spoke several foreign languages, were members of the Japan-Turkey Society whose honorary chair was Prince Takamatsu, and also loved horseback riding and dogs.

One of the reasons Ryusuke liked the house in Setagaya when he bought it was because of the very spacious dog house built under the mezzanine. Aka was a big dog and he needed a big house.

While they were walking, people stopped to look at Aka, as they had never seen a dog like this. They exclaimed "Oh, what is this animal? Is this a lion?" And each time, Ryusuke explained that it was a dog from Mongolia, and a supposedly ancient breed.

They arrived at the English style stone entrance of Marquis Maeda's mansion. The guard emerged from his small wooden building and ushered them onto the premises. A sinuous pathway winding through an English garden—led to the entrance of the brick Tudor mansion. At the entrance, an old butler was standing straight in a black tailcoat. It felt—as though they had suddenly been transported to England. When the butler approached to escort them inside, Ryusuke mentioned they could wait outside as they had a big dog with them.

The butler nodded with a smile and said: "Yes, sir. Marquis Maeda told me that you would be arriving with a Mongolian dog. Ladies, please come inside the entrance hall and have seats there," the butler said, and swung the door open for them. While he was talking, Marquis Maeda appeared from the side of the house, with a huge black dog and a house boy.

"Welcome, Yonezawa-san. Good afternoon, Mrs. Yonezawa," he greeted them with a friendly smile. Then he beamed down at the girls. Ryusuke introduced his daughters to Marquis Maeda.

"This is Yukiko and Masako. My eldest girl, Kinuko, has a concert at her school today, so she couldn't come. The boys are too little, so they stayed home."

"Oh, very nice to meet you, Yukiko-san and Masako-san. My daughter Miiko will be glad to see you."

Then his wife, Marchioness Maeda, and their daughter Miiko—came outside...that became quite lively, with the ladies and the girls chatting away while two

Mongolian dogs sniffed, barked, and wagged their tails.

"Look at them! They are so happy to see each other. Kuro and Aka, aren't they great?" asked Marquis Maeda.

"Yes, indeed. By the way, here is something for you. Matsutake mushrooms from Kyoto and some Russian confectionery shop's chocolate," said Ryusuke, and handed some packages to Marquis Maeda.

"Thank you very much. We love matsutake. The aroma is intoxicating. Thank you also for the wonderful chocolate. These chocolates are delicious," said Marquis Maeda.

"That is very kind of you," said Marchioness Maeda cheerfully, as she guided them to the garden.

"Shall we sit on the terrace and have tea? Kinoshita, can you keep your eyes on these dogs while we sit at a table?" Marchioness Maeda asked the houseboy, and led the Yonezawas to the elevated stone terrace that featured an elegant English style table and chairs. Then she handed the presents to the butler and he brought them back to the house.

They all sat at the table and watched the dogs running and jumping together in the huge front garden. Kinoshita was standing nearby to make sure that they didn't fight or run into the flower garden, though it seemed there was no need to worry.

"Maybe they are remembering their homeland! Look how fast they run! It is easy to have them together. They can have a race. You should bring him over often," said Marquis Maeda with a smile.

"I agree. I will come with him more often," answered Ryusuke.

The butler and two maids wheeled in a cart with tea, scones with cream and jam, cakes and cookies, and served them.

Marquis Maeda was the 16th head of the Maeda clan. Though there was no actual Maeda clan, more than 100 people working for the Marquis's family were all from the area that had previously housed the Maeda estate. There seemed to be a strong bond; almost as if it were one household. The butlers had been chosen from the former ministers' families and their manners were truly like classic retainers serving their lords.

The Maeda clan had long had their estate in Hongo, Bunkyo district, in central Tokyo. In 1885, when the Tokyo Imperial University extended its campus and acquired the former Maeda estate, the government gave a part of the Komaba campus (another campus in Meguro) to Marquis Maeda in exchange. The new property, including farms, was so huge, that even after Marquis Maeda received his big estate, a part of the farm still remained and used for the agricultural division of the university.

This place–the Komaba campus–was where professor Ueno taught civil engineering. He also made business trips to other locations. Professor Ueno went to the Komaba campus on foot, and Hachiko always accompanied him. Hachiko would loll about the big field of the Komaba campus until the professor finished his lectures and returned home with him in the evening. Just as Aka and Kuro were romping in the garden nearby, so Hachiko cavorted about the Komaba campus until professor Ueno finished his lectures.

When professor Ueno taught at some other locations or made business trips, Hachiko accompanied him to Shibuya station in the morning and returned at evening time to come home with him. In the case of several-day business trips, Hachiko would still appear at the station every day; not knowing how long his master would be gone. But understanding that shortly...he would return.

***

After tea and conversation, the Marchioness suggested she show them their Japanese house and also her new kimono. "I imagine you ladies would be interested in looking at my new kimonos. The kimono artists finished them and they were delivered yesterday. They are on display stands in the Japanese room," she explained.

Marquis Maeda added a humorous expression. "My wife loves to design kimonos with sceneries of foreign countries. Whenever there are receptions with foreign ambassadors, she makes kimonos with a setting from their land. Can you imagine how many ambassadors are in Japan now?"

"Not from every country," she laughed.

Motoko replied agreeably. "It's a wonderful way to show appreciation. And please the eyes, as well, on such occasions."

"You are right. These kimonos are truly works of arts. And just imagine: encountering a picture of the Matterhorn, on a kimono!" replied Marquis Maeda with a smile.

They strolled to the Japanese house, chatting away; an imposing traditional two-storied traditional dwelling with a Japanese garden that made good use of the natural surroundings. The quiet garden with pines and maples created an atmosphere of being deep within a mountain fastness. Several large tatami rooms surrounded by a corridor—faced out onto the garden. Screens dividing the rooms—were flung open, that the room covered an area of perhaps 40 tatami mats. It felt cavernous.

A dark blue carpet filled the center, exposing the tatami mats around the perimeter. Two sets of gorgeous kimonos hung from their kimono stands and trailed on the carpet like the downside of a wave returning to the blue sea. One garment—depicting a cream and white-colored Matterhorn—stood out against an azure sky. At the foot of the mountain, a field of pink and yellow flowers stretched toward the horizon. The entire scene—so artistic—reminded one of an oil painting.

The other garment was of midnight blue; recreating Venice at sunset. A black gondola and the white Basilica di San Marco on Grand Canal, against an orange sky, were meticulously embroidered; their gold and silver threads reflecting on the water.

"These are gorgeous!" exclaimed Motoko.

"What a creative idea: integrating western settings into the kimono," exclaimed Ryusuke.

Marquis Maeda's daughter, Miiko, was about 5 years old and had grown up in London. She was very cute and her face dimpled when she smiled. She spoke English fluently, and though little, she seemed to have learned social manners already. She was eager to show Yukiko and Masako her doll collection. She called her nanny, who led the girls to a nursery in the western house. Marchioness Maeda and Motoko were sitting on chairs in a corridor and talking. Marquis Maeda and Ryusuke stepped outside to the Japanese garden and strolled under autumn foliage chatting.

"Have you seen Baron Nishi recently?" asked Ryusuke.

"Yes. I saw him and his belovéd horse, Uranus, at the 16th Narashino Cavalry Regiment," answered Marquis Maeda.

"It was really a great feat: his winning the gold medal in the individual show jumping at the Los Angeles Olympics," said Ryusuke.

"Yes. It was exciting. He became a celebrity in Los Angeles. Did you see the picture of his car in Los Angeles?"

"Oh, you mean the gold Packard convertible? What a car! Baron Nishi cuts a very good figure. I bet he was very popular in Hollywood."

"I heard he partied with Mary Pickford and Douglas Fairbanks," said Marquis Maeda.

"Really?" answered Ryusuke, bright-eyed in amazement, and added:

"He must have felt comfortable in America. He is liberal and flamboyant; something not too well-suited to Japanese society; especially in the military,"

"You are right. He stands out a little too...prominently. In the army, the nail that sticks out gets hammered down," replied Marquis Maeda.

"Well, I have to say that it is the same here, and you're very right?" said Ryusuke, as they both looked at each other and laughed.

Ryusuke had ordered an English tailor to make his military suits for better fitting; causing some raised eyebrows; Marquis Maeda was famous for his outspokenness to his bosses. They both stood out in the army; and made several enemies—and thus appreciated this heart-to-heart talk whenever they met.

"By the way, the Japanese swim team competed very well. Four gold medals was such an accomplishment," said Ryusuke.

"Right. Everyone is so proud of them. Do you know Johnny Weissmuller opened the swimming pool of the Tobacco king, Mr. Chiba?"

"Oh, I didn't know that. Is there a swimming pool at Mr. Chiba's house?" asked Ryusuke.

"Yes. I was invited to their house in Aoyama recently. There was a beautiful pool in the basement, and the plaque fixed to the floor saying 'Johnny Weissmuller opened this pool in 1928'."

"We often pass by that gothic mansion of Mr. Chiba when we visit our ancestors' graves in Aoyama cemetery. It looks like a castle with that round tower."

"It does. There is a fountain with a lion's head, inside! I wasn't in Japan in 1928, so I didn't know about it. But I heard that Johnny Weissmuller, Arne Borg, and several other foreign gold medalists were invited for the competition in Japan. They also attended friendship events and Johnny Weissmuller took the first swim at Mr. Chiba's pool. Mr. Chiba told me he was a very kind gentleman," replied Marquis Maeda.

"That must have been quite a party. My wife sends our boys to swim school and makes all our children drink a lot of milk. This is all Johnny Weissmuller's influence! It is wonderful that people are interested in sports these days. Girls are becoming very active too," said Ryusuke.

"That's right! My daughter, Miiko, is a tomboy. She jumped out a window to the garden and that old nanny had to run to the garden door to catch up with her," laughed Marquis Maeda.

"She is athletic! Look, the first lord, Maeda Toshiie was so brave and athletic. Miiko-san takes after him," said Ryusuke, and laughed.

***

It was time to leave. Ryusuke and Motoko went to the front yard of the western house to get Aka. The girls came out to the garden. Marchioness Maeda, the girls and the nanny all walked to the front yard. Ryusuke received Aka from Kinoshita. Aka wagged his tail and jumped to Ryusuke. Kuro cried with a sad whimper as he understood that Aka was leaving. Marquis Maeda sat next to Kuro and patted him gently. The girls were saying good-by to each other. Ryusuke pulled the reins of Aka as he still played with Kuro and didn't want to move. Finally, the Yonezawas said good-by to everybody and left Marquis Maeda's estate.

The day was warm and sunny. A slight breeze beckoned—inviting all who heard it, to follow, wherever it might lead. They decided to stroll about Shibuya. The area had an elegant atmosphere. Among traditional houses were quite a few with refined western designs. All, a feast for the eyes. Ryusuke and Motoko chatted as passed these lofty mansions.

Some of the princely dwellings were so huge you could recognize them by their entrances. These princes' estates had either Japanese traditional style gates or western style gates and were surrounded by high walls. In the case of Japanese-style gates, one faced the street; a long gabled path then led to a second formal gate. It looked like a big shrine or temple.

Aristocratic families and a group of Japanese intellectuals who lived overseas—built very sophisticated European houses in Shibuya. The styles of houses varied according to individual taste: Tudor, Spanish,

German, French renaissance, Gothic, Art Deco, Colonial. It was like walking through a book on architectural design.

Mr. Sadatsuchi Uchida, who served as consul general in New York, high commissioner to the Ottoman Empire, and the founder of the Japan-Turkey society–built an elegant mansion in Shibuya. His ancestor was a samurai from Kyushu, and Ryusuke became acquainted with him through his Kyushu connection as well as his Turkish connection. The mansion was designed by an American architect, James Gardner, and was in completely western style. The cream yellow house accented with dark brown window frames and gutters–was in American Victorian; with a touch of American Arts and Crafts style. The three-storied octagonal tower with a pointed roof was a well-known landmark in the neighborhood.

There were several foreign architects living in Japan, who designed western style houses at that time. Antonin Raymond, who was originally from Czechoslovakia and became an American citizen, came to Japan as an assistant to Frank Lloyd Wright in 1919. He stayed on after the Imperial hotel was completed, and designed many houses, including the beautiful American Ambassador's official residence in Akasaka, Minato district, built in 1931.

7

Statue of Hachiko & Pilgrim Dogs

On a Sunday afternoon in January 1934, Motoko and the children were sitting in the living
room and having cakes and tea. Ryusuke was
out for a meeting at Gajoen, in Meguro (a popular
Japanese and Chinese restaurant referred to as 'the
dragon king's palace' because of its gorgeous decora-
tion done by the artists of that time).

The sound of the shamisen (the three-stringed Japanese musical instrument) and the singing voices of
Tei and her students were heard from Tei's room.
Tei had been teaching Tokiwazu (a style of narrative
and singing for kabuki plays). She sometimes practiced Tokiwazu singing at a clothes-drying platform
on the roof of the house. She said it was the best
way to improve her voice. The neighboring houses

were not close, so her practice did not bother the people living near by. However, people noticed her singing and she became quite famous as a Tokiwazu instructor. Many people asked for lessons and her room became lively with her students several times a week.

After the lesson, Tei came to the living room and joined the group for tea. She talked about the news of setting up a statue of Hachiko at Shibuya station. Her student told her about the details.

"Mrs. Takano told me that a noted sculptor, Mr. Teru Ando, will make the statue of Hachiko. Mr. Ando made a plaster figure of Hachiko and exhibited it at the Imperial Academy Exhibition last year and it was very popular. The gardener, Kikusaburo, took Hachiko to Teru's studio for modeling. Hachiko was very cooperative and the statue came out a strong likeness. Therefore, 'the statue of Hachiko committee' asked Mr. Ando formally to make the sculpture."

"I read the article in a newspaper recently, on them setting up a statue of Hachiko. I was just thinking to send a donation. We all know Hachiko very well and admire his loyalty. It is fitting they set up a statue, so that everyone will know about his noble and loyal heart," answered Motoko.

"It is amazing that a statue will be set up in his honor. Hachiko is still alive. Isn't it quite unusual to set up a statue when the person is still alive? " asked Kinuko.

"It is quite unusual. That is how much people admire Hachiko. He has been treated nicely these days, though until he became famous, there were bad people who were mean to him," said Tei.

The Yonezawas had heard about Hachiko's situation from their neighbor when they moved to Shibuya in 1929. Those who knew Hachiko since he accompanied professor Ueno–understood the reason why he always waited at Shibuya station. The story of the loyal Hachiko spread and people in the town recognized him. However, there were some who shoved him away or kicked him at Shibuya station. Once, a mischievous person painted glasses and a mustache on his face with brush ink and laughed at him. Even though, Hahciko sat quietly and let him draw on his face. He was a gentle dog.

Mr. Kokichi Saito, who was a researcher on dogs, had known Hachiko for a long time. He thought people should know about Hachiko's sad circumstances and teach people to be kind to him. In October of 1931, he wrote an article 'A story of a poor old dog, waiting for his deceased master for 7 years' in a national newspaper. The story touched people hearts. Some brought food for him, sent letters with donations to the stationmaster, and many at Shibuya station came to look upon him warmly. Now Hachiko could stay in the station anywhere without being chased away. In summer, he could rest in a cool place and in winter he could warm himself near a stove in the station.

"I think Hachiko will become famous," said Yukiko.

"Oh, yes. I heard that in March, there will be an event called 'An evening with Hachiko' at the outer garden of the Meiji shrine, to raise money for the statue. There will be a play, dance, and music. Hachiko will be attending too," said Tei.

"Really? He is like a movie star! Will he be all right in a place like that?" asked Takao.

"He is close to the stationmaster and therefore he will be fine attending the event if the stationmaster is with him. Hachiko is accustomed to being among many people as he always sits at Shibuya station," answered Tei and she continued.

"Have you heard of pilgrim dogs?"

"What are they? " asked the children curiously.

"Hachiko and people surrounding him reminded me of the pilgrim dogs of the Edo period," said Tei.

"I've heard of them. These dogs In olden times, they made pilgrimages to Ise shrine (a very important Shinto shrine complex in the city of Mie prefecture) by themselves. Owners who couldn't go on the Ise shrine pilgrimage sent their dogs instead. Isn't that a wonder," exclaimed Motoko.

"But, how? How did the dogs find the way to Ise?" asked Sadao.

"Let me tell you. I know about the pilgrim dogs," Tei smiled and started to explain.

"According to several old historic documents, the dogs' Ise shrine pilgrimages started in the late 18th century. Those zealous pilgrims who could not go because of illness or some reasons–sent their dogs with letters that explained the purpose of the trip (visiting the shrine), with money attached to their collars, and sent them on the long journey. Someone traveling in the same direction would fall in with the dog and guide him to an inn at the next stop.

The innkeeper gave the dog food and a place to sleep, collected money for the fee (payment instructions were written in the letters), and asked someone heading in the same direction–to guide him. In old days, people traveled in a more leisurely fashion, and someone always volunteered to accompany the dog to the next way station. Sometimes, innkeepers didn't receive money from the dog or sometimes people who were impressed by the dog's sincere attitude gave money to the dog. If the money attached to his collar became too heavy, someone exchanged the money for a few valuable coins instead of many small coins.

Everyone loved to help pilgrim dogs and nobody took money from them. Assisted by these kind travelers, the dogs would arrive at Ise shrine after weeks or even months of long trips. The priest would give them blessings, tie amulets wrapped in waterproof papers to their collars, and send them home. People respected pilgrim dogs. When the dogs finished the pilgrimages, somebody at the shrine would check the direction of their homes written in the letters and help them get there. The dogs would travel days to their homes to see their masters and give them the amulets. Of course, the masters would greet the dogs with joy and the dogs became heroes. These were the pilgrim dogs," explained Tei.

"Wow, they were so smart! It is fun to imagine a dog carrying a letter and money traveling by itself to the-Ise shrine," said Kinuko.

"They must have looked so cute," said Masako. Tei smiled and nodded in agreement.

"You will find drawings of pilgrim dogs in the old books. I heard some of them even bowed to the shrine!" said Tei with laughter.

"They just bowed by chance, but people thought the dogs actually showed their respect to the shrine. That was funny," said Motoko.

"People helped the dogs because they were impressed by their sincere attitude to help their masters. I also think many people enjoyed traveling with gentle animals. People in the old days walked long distance to reach their destination. It must had been fun for them to have company," said Tei.

"Dogs are smart and love to work. The Ise pilgrimage must have been fun for dogs, too!" said Yukiko.

"I wish they would still do the pilgrimage. When did they stop doing this?" asked Masako. Tei responded, looking at the children.

"It was over when the Meiji government made the rule to control stray animals. The dogs couldn't travel by themselves anymore. In the Edo era, everything was slow and easy. People regarded stray dogs as belonging to their community and took care of them. Dogs were treated nicely and therefore they didn't normally attack or bite people."

"Hachiko could have been a pilgrim dog if he was born in the Edo era," said Takao.

"Yes. He could have been an excellent pilgrim dog. Interestingly, people during the Edo era believed that white dogs possessed magical power. Therefore, most of the Ise pilgrim dogs were white. Hachiko would have been the perfect candidate," answered Tei.

"I heard that during the Edo era people used dogs to do their errands. For example, shopping or delivering things to their friends! A well-trained dog understood the name of the shop he had to go to. The owner attached a letter and money to the dog's collar and directed him to go to the shop. The shopkeeper would read the letter, attach the goods to the collar, take the money, and send him back home. People were used to this custom. That was why the dog pilgrimage was possible. From early times, people knew that dogs were so smart," said Motoko.

"That is fun! I wish Aka could go shopping for us!" exclaimed Sadao.

"He would be good. But people are afraid of him. He can't do it," said Motoko, and laughed; imagining a big Mongolian dog shopping on Shibuya street."

"Wait a moment. I have a few old books with pictures of the pilgrim dogs," said Tei, and she went to her room to get them.

She soon returned with several old Edo era books. She searched for the pictures, found them, and showed them to the children. One page displayed a picture of a dog with a wooden name plate, a letter, and a sack of coins attached to his collar, walking on the famous Nihonbashi bridge. A fish merchant weighed down with two baskets of catch balanced on a carrying-pole–hurried along, pursued by several cats.

Old Nihonbashi never looked so good. Still another book revealed a picture of several dogs walking in front of the shops on the main street near the Ise shrine. The dogs carried letters and money in their collars. A shop lady was giving some food to the dogs and people looked on. In another book, a dog could be walking next to a palanquin in which a high-class samurai was sitting and watching him.

The children talked and laughed while looking at the books.

"Wow, this is Nihonbashi! A dog walked from Nihonbashi to Ise! That must have taken so long!" said Yukiko. Tei responded fondly with a smile.

"Oh, these dogs traveled from Aomori (the northern part of mainland Japan), Nagano (the mountainous area of central Japan), Tokyo and many far away places all the way to Ise. I heard a funny story when I was little. One pilgrim dog whose foot was hurt accidently–mingled in a lord's grand procession. On the way home, a retainer noticed the dog was a pilgrim dog, going in the same direction as the lord's estate. When the retainer told this to the lord, who loved dogs, he ordered the retainers to carry the dog on a palanquin. Several retainers put a soft cushion on a palanquin and let the dog sit on it. The lucky dog was carried all the way to his home on a palanquin, as a part of a grand procession."

Everyone laughed at this story.

Figure 10: The original statue of Hachiko circa 1934.

At this time, Yukiko had begun going to Futaba Women's School in Yotsuya. Therefore, Kinuko and Yukiko used Shibuya station every day, to change train to Yotsuya. Masako and Takao went to Omukai elementary school in Shibuya. For Kinuko, Yukiko, Masako and Takao, Hachiko became so familiar as if he was their dog. Every day, they saw him at Shibuya station, and patted him whenever they had the chance. Sometimes Hachiko smiled and looked happy. He couldn't see professor Ueno, but there were many people who cared about him. The shopkeepers of the small shops were very kind to him too. At that time there were several other stray dogs at Shibuya station. Thanks to Hachiko's popularity, they also received food and were treated nicely. Hachiko was like the boss of these stray dogs. The reason that one of his ears was bent was because he was bitten while he tried to stop a fight between two other dogs. He defended a weaker dog in the pack. Considerate relations between dogs and people around Shibuya station were like those of the community dogs and people in the old Edo era.

On March 10th 'An Evening with Hachiko' was held in the outer garden of the Meiji shrine. The Yonezawa children went to see the event with Motoko and Kiyo. After a play and dance, Hachiko appeared on the stage with the stationmaster and greeted the audience. More than 3000 attendees clapped their hands for Hachiko and the event ended successfully.

On April 21st, the statue of Hachiko was unveiled. Hachiko wore red and white scarves while attending the ceremony. The sitting statue of Hachiko was made by Teru Ando on a tall pedestal, and was shown to the public. The area was decorated with red and white banners and many floral garlands. Many people celebrated this event with Hachiko. From this day on, Hachiko could be seen, waiting for his master at Shibuya station; seating beside his own statue. To an occasional passer-by, it seemed like a living being, seated alongside his image.

Friendship with Turkish People

Ryusuke started to work for the Turkish Embassy in Tokyo in 1934. He liked his new job and devoted himself to building good relations between the two countries.

He got along well with his former boss at the military—general Jo Iimura. But Ryusuke was disliked by other high officials in the army, and felt relieved when he was forced into early retirement. General Iimura and Ryusuke had several things in common. Both spoke French and Turkish, and were members of the Japan-Turkey Society. General Iimura taught at the Turkish Military College in Istanbul when he was a military attaché to Turkey. In addition general Iimura, like Ryusuke, had a good sense of humor, and liked singing French chansons. Therefore, they kept their friendship after Ryusuke left the army, and worked together for Japan-Turkey relations.

At that time, the Turkish Embassy in Tokyo was located in Shoto, Shibuya. It was a beautiful English Tudor style mansion surrounded by a huge garden. Sometimes, Ryusuke would ask his foreign student guests to take walks with the Mongolian dog, Aka and him, to the embassy. This way, he could let Aka exercise. Then, after Ryusuke said good-by at the entrance of the embassy, the students would walk Aka to Nabeshima park and then home. At that time, people in Tokyo kept big dogs such as Akitas and Tosas, St.Bernards and Dobermans, as they needed guards dogs. You often saw men or houseboys walking them at all hours.

Nabeshima park was redolent, and Turkish people living in Shibuya often went there. When the Yonezawas ran into Turks at the park, they greeted each other in mixed expressions of Turkish and French, like "Bonjour, canım (sweetie)" or "Bonsoir, hayatım (darling)." Many Turks living in Tokyo at the time spoke French, and mentioned it was fashionable to greet people that way in Istanbul. The Yonezawas adopted the custom in Shibuya, and spread it to other friends who lived near by. Some friends from Futaba Women's School, whose fathers worked for the Turkish embassy, also lived in Shibuya. They quickly adopted this new fashion, so that the gentle sounds of French and Turkish were often heard intermingled at Nabeshima park.

The Yonezawas occasionally had Turkish guests to their house. And especially since Ryusuke started working at the Turkish embassy, more Turkish people dropped by, and all had great times together.

Lieutenant Rüştü Erdelhün was a military attaché at the embassy. Şeref Karapınar and Zeki Bayat were naval officers and were students sent to Japan by the Turkish government for the memorial of Ertuğrul incident.

The program was initiated between the two countries several years earlier, to memorialize the sinking of the Ottoman frigate Ertuğrul. The disaster occurred outside the Kashinozaki lighthouse on the Kii peninsula of Wakayama prefecture in 1890. The Ottoman frigate Ertuğrul visited Japan to deliver a letter from Sultan Abdul Hamit II to the Meiji Emperor. Unfortunately, on its return, the ship was stranded by a typhoon. The Japanese fishermen in the village tried very hard to rescue them, but 587 of the people aboard were lost. However, 69 were rescued in severe rain, and wind, and the villagers took very good care of them. The villagers rescued the bodies of the dead and conducted a memorial for them. The survivors were sent back to Turkey on the Japanese warships the Hie and the Kongo, in October of that year. It was a sad incident, but the Turks greatly appreciated the rescue by the Japanese people. As a result, Japan-Turkey relations blossomed. It was an honor for Turkish naval officers to be sent to Japan as Ertuğrul students, and they worked very hard. Both Şeref and Zeki spoke good Japanese.

Zeki Bayat was close to Ryusuke, and he came to their house very often. Reşat, a young Turkish teenage boy working for the embassy, visited almost daily. It seemed he enjoyed meeting foreign students of his age at Ryusuke's house. Rüştü was a great horseback rider, and Ryusuke enjoyed taking him to the Setagaya cavalry division to ride together. When he came back he always said "Rüştü-san's handling of the reins was incredible. He is truly from an equestrian people!"

Another guest who was involved with Turkey often came to their house. Professor Koji Okubo was a well-known scholar of Turkey and Islam. He was teaching Turkish at the Tokyo University of Foreign Studies and the Japan-Turkey society. Professor Okubo also made friends with Tatars who escaped Russia after the 1917 revolution and settled in Oyama-cho, Shibuya. There were several hundred Tatars living in Shibuya at that time. The Tatar language is similar to Turkish. Thus, professor Okubo could help these exiles, with his Turkish skills. He was very knowledgeable, and Ryusuke enjoyed his company greatly. With all these people around, the children became accustomed to speaking Turkish.

Both Şeref and Zeki were interested in studying Japanese culture and martial arts. Ryusuke sometimes took them to Japanese archery lessons.

One day, Ryusuke came home and said: "Today we made Zeki-san and Şeref-san wear hakama (Japanese traditional trousers) and practiced archery. They looked very good in hakama."

"How are they doing with archery? " asked Kinuko.

"They were strong and had very good control. They did well. They were tall so it was hard to find the hakama and bows that fit them," answered Ryusuke.

"Oh, yes. They are very tall. Didn't the hakama look short on them?" laughed Takao.

"Yes. But they looked really brilliant. Fortunately, we had long bows for them," replied Ryusuke. "By the way," he added, "Zeki-san and I want to do a Japanese and Turkish conversation book and publish it."

"Really? That is very interesting," said Motoko.

"Very much so. No such a book exists yet. It will be very helpful. We want to do a book that both Japanese and Turks can use. Zeki-san will come to our house often for this project."

Shortly after that, Zeki began to visit regularly, to work on the project. Sometimes, professor Okubo and Jo Iimura joined the meeting. Rüştü and Reşat contributed from time to time. As there was no study aid book for Turkish and Japanese, they had to spend a lot of time figuring out correct translations in both languages. In the book, they wrote each sentence with the Turkish language written in Japanese and Japanese language written in the Turkish alphabet, so that Turkish people who couldn't read Japanese could use the book. It was hard work, though they enjoyed it very much.

Figure 11: ZekiBayat (second from the right) practicing kyudo (Japanese archery), circa 1937.

Every year in late May or early June, the Japan-Turkey society held annual meetings. This year, they met on May 28th at Tokyo Kaikan, with the presence of the honorary chair, Prince Takamatsu, who was a brother of Emperor Showa. Tokyo Kaikan was an international assembly hall and hotel near Tokyo station, and the five-story Renaissance building was gorgeous. Ryusuke and Zeki had a wonderful time with the members.

Sometimes, the Yonezawas were invited to Zeki's house. He was renting an annex of an old temple. The house was in Japanese style but some of the rooms were carpeted and furnished with western style furniture. At that time, foreign families with children rented western style houses—quite a few were available in Tokyo. Singles or couples who didn't need big houses often rented annexes of large estates or temples.

One day, Zeki mentioned that his dog had puppies, and asked if the Yonezawas would like one. They agreed and Motoko and the three girls went to his house to pick one out. When they arrived at Zeki's house, he took them to a dog house in the yard. A white Shiba Inu mother was lying about, with three puppies. They were three months old. The children looked at the puppies and talked about which one to adopt. It took quite a long time to decide but finally they chose a light brown one. It had very cute eyes and looked like a fox. The name of the puppy was 'Yıldız', which means 'star' in Turkish. The names of the other two dogs were 'Güneş (sun)' and 'Ay (moon)'. After that, they were invited to the living room. An old Japanese maid working for Zeki brought Turkish tea in tulip-shaped cups and some cookies.

"Yıldız is so cute!" "She is so adorable!" the children kept saying while drinking tea.

"I think Aka and Yıldız will get along well," said Motoko.

"Aka is a gentle dog and she will be nice to her. She needs company, so that is very good," said Zeki.

"Zeki-san. Do you know Hachiko at Shibuya station?" asked Yukiko.

"Yes, of course. He is such a loyal dog. Every time I go to the Turkish embassy, I see him at Shibuya station.

I was impressed that now his statue has been built. He will be known all over the world!" answered Zeki.

"Really? It would be amazing if people in foreign countries knew about Hachiko!" said Kinuko.

"Sometimes I see foreigners taking pictures of Hachiko. He is already well-known among foreigners living in Tokyo. By the way, we have guardian dogs called Kangals in Turkey. Hachiko reminds me of a Kangal. His long strong legs, curled tail, short thick fur, and close bonding with the owners reminds me of that Turkish dog breed," said Zeki.

"Wow, what kind of dog is that?" asked the children.

"It is an ancient breed. It is pale tan, with a black muzzle and black drooping ears. Although very big, they have cute faces. They have long legs and when they stand up on their hind legs they are the same height as me," answered Zeki.

"Wow, that must be tall! " said Masako as her eyes popped out in astonishment.

"Yes. But they are loyal and affectionate, just like Aka and Hachiko," said Zeki. As they all loved dogs, the conversation went on for quite a while.

Shortly after, Motoko noticed a leather bound book on the table, and next to it several papers with many names written in kanji (Chinese characters).

"Did you write these?" she asked.

"Yes," answered Zeki. He opened the book to show them the business cards organized in it. Then, he continued.

"Whenever I receive business cards, I practice writing the names in kanji. That is the reason for those papers."

"Oh, these are beautifully written. Your calligraphy is very good. It must have taken a long time to learn these," said Motoko. There were many difficult characters that even Japanese people would have a hard time to write. Motoko and the children looked at the papers and the business cards in turn and admired Zeki's writing.

"It is hard, though it is fun too. After memorizing radicals, I can write many characters, combining them with other parts. Sometimes, I create my own characters by mistake!" said Zeki as he laughed.

The leather bound business card folder was equipped with special tweezers to organize cards. The children were impressed by the interesting stationary.

After finishing tea, they went to the yard with Zeki and picked up Yıldız. Motoko held her in a blanket. It was hard to take her from the mother, but they managed to do so. Then, they said good-by to Zeki and took a taxi home.

"I think daddy and Zeki-san's Japanese and Turkish book will be a very good one!" said Yukiko. Motoko answered with a smile.

"I was thinking the same thing. Zeki-san is such a hard worker, I'm sure the book will be successful. He is both a good warrior and a good scholar."

It was late afternoon. A tofu seller's horn (tofu sell-
ers used to walk around the residential area blowing
horns to promote their products) was heard from
somewhere in a quiet street lined with old houses.
The sound had a sadness and nostalgia to it. Motoko held Yıldız like a baby so the puppy wouldn't
be scared by the vibration of the car. The three girls
kept looking over the puppy with smiles. Yildiz was
looking back at the girls with a peaceful expression.

Architecture of Tokyo

*I*n the 1930s, Tokyo was a beautiful mixture of western style architecture and traditional Edo period wooden houses. Many foreigners were charmed by this unusual combination and enjoyed living in there.

One Sunday in June of 1934, Ryusuke, Noel, and Zeki were lunching at Tokyo Kaikan, near Tokyo station. Zeki and Noel had met at Ryusuke's house and became good friends. Today, they decided to do a tour around the palace, as Noel knew the area very well. For many years, Noel had done a slow circumambulation of the palace, sketchbook in hand, and made many drawings. He also published books on the history of Edo and Tokyo. He knew Tokyo very well in detail.

The three came out from the gray and apricot-colored French-style building and stood by a moat. It was slightly overcast, but a comfortable day for a walk. Looking at the scene by a moat, they talked.

"That was a delicious lunch. How many French restaurants are in Tokyo now?" Zeki asked. Ryusuke and Noel looked at each other and tried to count the number.

Noel admitted: "I don't know them all. But, let's see, Seiyoken in Ueno, Tokyo Kaikan here, Shiseido Parlor in Ginza, the Imperial Hotel, these are run by big companies. There are French restaurants run by families such as Ryuduken, in Azabu. The officers clubs have French restaurants. All in all, quite a crop," Noel said.

"I go to Ryudoken often. It is situated near the army facilities, and the officers like the restaurant very much. Zeki-san, let's go there next time," said Ryusuke.

"Thank you very much, Ryusuke-san. I stayed at the Imperial Hotel for a week after I arrived at Tokyo. The design is really unique. I loved the pond. The artistic stone architecture resembles a Mayan temple," Zeki answered.

"It was designed by an American architect, Frank Lloyd Wright. You are right, Zeki-san. It does looks like a Mayan temple. It also looks like the Byodo-in temple in Kyoto. He made a unique design. Surprisingly, the Great Kanto earthquake of 1923 occurred during the opening ceremony of the hotel! But there was no damage, thanks to its clever structural design and careful choice of materials. Other buildings in the surrounding area were damaged terribly," answered Noel.

"Oh, really? I can imagine," answered Zeki.

"Speaking of a hotel, Yukiko said they went to Tokyo Mampei Hotel in Kojimachi, for her girls' school manner class. She said it was a beautiful hotel and the restaurant was very fancy," said Ryusuke.

"I've heard of it. Karuizawa Mampai Hotel opened a branch in Tokyo. It's situated very close to Futaba Women's School. Kojimachi became very European," Noel said.

The Futaba Women's School, a French Catholic school where Yukiko went, was situated in Kojimachi, near Yotsuya station. The school building was designed by a Czech architect, Jan Letzel, who had an architectural firm on the Ginza. The school had a symmetrical Neo-Renaissance style, with a gymnasium, a nunnery, and church with a Gothic style tower. The main building was yellow with green trimmings, and the hall was decorated with stained glass. The Futaba Women's School in Kojimachi was referred to as one of the most beautiful buildings at the time.

Figure 12: The water towers in Setagaya-ku, circa 1932, The two towers were connected by a truss bridge and decorated with beautiful lighting fixtures. They were lit up at night.

"Noel-san, do you know the twin water towers in Setagaya? We sometimes pass the towers when we take Aka for a long walk. They remind me of medieval European castles," Ryusuke asked.

Noel answered: "Oh, the towers connected by a truss bridge? They look very stylish with the glove shaped lights on top of them."

"Yes, we call them 'crowns on the hill'. The lights are light purple. They stir the imaginations of passerbys," Ryusuke said.

Noel responded curiously. "I didn't know the lights are purple. That must look beautiful. I will go see them in the evening next time."

"I would like to join you. I enjoy taking pictures of interesting architecture," said Zeki holding his German camera proudly.

Zeki carried a camera while walking and stopped sometimes to take pictures. They walked by a moat and arrived at Sakurada gate where the famous 'Sakurada gate incident' occurred. Ryusuke explained: "Ii Naosuke, the lord of the Hikone clan and the Shogun's aide–who signed the treaty to open Japan to the world–were assassinated by groups of samurai who were against the decision. It was on a snowy day in March of 1860. It was the beginning of numerous many incidents that led to civil war.

"These are great gates (Sakurada gate consisted of two gates: an inner and outer one);" Zeki admired the gates and took pictures.

"I like to draw these gates. Standing before them, I sometimes close my eyes, and imagine opening them to find groups of samurai pattering across the bridge. Or a feudal lord's procession crossing the span and disappearing into the gates. Not much has changed since the 16th century."

"That must have been quite a spectacle," Zeki said.

"Yes. Those foreigners who lived in Tokyo at the end of the Edo era described the grandeur of the samurai processions to Edo castle, and the formal audiences that took place within," answered Noel.

"Samurais' kimonos were in dark colors with fine patterns. Their refined colors stood out against the gray stones, the whitewashed walls, and green pine trees in Edo castle," explained Ryusuke.

For formal occasions, samurai wore a special vest called a 'Kamishimo', over the kimono. The Kamishimo was dyed with fine patterns of each clan and the family crest. Accordingly, you could recognize the samurai's clan by looking at the pattern. These kimono patterns looked harmonious when mingled with other patterns. On top of the kimono they wore an obi (a sash or belt). Kuroda Nagamasa (1568-1623) of the Kuroda clan presented an artistic obi from Fukuoka, to the Tokugawa shogun. It was called a Hakata kenjo obi (Hakata was the name of the place where the obi was made and 'kenjo' means offering to high ranking people). Since then, the lords of the Kuroda clan had been offering Hakata kenjo obi to the Tokugawa shoguns during the Edo period, and the Hakata kenjo obi had become sought-after items. The combination of Edo komon kimono (kimono dyed with special techniques in Edo) with Hakata kenjo obi was regarded as the most formal for samurai during the Edo period.

They continued their walk and finally arrived at an area near Tokyo station: one of the modern sections of 1930s Tokyo. It was a stark contrast. On the one hand: the traditional Japanese moats, with their brooding castles—dark, impenetrable; exuding power. One the other: the European style architecture, with their own grandeur, but slightly insouciant and inviting.

The three-story red brick station building was designed by Kingo Tatsuno and completed in 1914. Many western style office buildings stood in this area. In fact, there was a street called 'iccho (the Japanese old unit of length was 109 meters) London' and an ' iccho New York' as these streets resembled London and New York around that time.

The three stopped before the Central Post Office, which was completed in 1931. The white modern concrete structure stood out among the red brick buildings.

"This avant-garde architecture was designed by Tetsuro Yoshida. Doesn't it look plain?" Noel asked.

"Yes, it is. It is an eye-opening discovery that such modern architecture was built in Tokyo. It was fun looking at all these different designs from different times," Zeki said.

"Me too. I enjoyed the tour very much. I haven't paid much attention to the scenery around the moat, as I have known it for a long time. After today's walk, I will appreciate it much more. Thank you very much, Noel-san. It was very interesting. Now I know why you like to walk around Tokyo," Ryusuke said.

"My pleasure, Ryusuke-san and Zeki-san. Are you hungry?" Noel asked.

The three decided to go somewhere for dinner, and walked to Tokyo station. The sky had cleared, and the evening glow tinctured the tips of the trees about the palace.

The Last Garden Party

One of the charming characteristics of the 1930s in Tokyo was that there were still many former lords' castles remaining from the Edo period.

During that period, the feudal lords and their successor (usually the eldest son) had to live in the castle of their domain and in the residence in Edo every other year, by the Edo shogun's writ. Their wives and other children had to live in the Edo mansions all year round—as hostages. The wives and children lived luxurious life styles, but the shoguns kept them in Edo so that the lords could not rebel against them. When the lords traveled back and forth between their castles and the Edo residences, they had to make elaborate processions, as decreed by shogun's law. The costly procession had economic effects on the local community, as hundreds of members of these processions dined and stayed at inns along the way, whose cost was paid by the lords.

At that time the lords had several estates in Edo. A main castle, a retired lord's house, a villa, and so on. After the Meiji restoration, many of their residences were taken by the government and transformed into government offices. However, the former lords were given aristocratic titles and could keep some of their mansions in Tokyo. As a result, many traditional estates with beautiful gardens were seen here and there in Tokyo during the 1930s.

The lord of the Kuroda's main dwelling—in Chiyoda district had become the Ministry of Foreign Affairs. In the 1930s, the 13th lord of the Kuroda clan, Nagashige Kuroda, or Marquis Kuroda, lived at a former villa at Tameike, in the Minato district—now a modern skyscraper. This estate had a large Japanese garden and a big duck pond. Nagashige had a son, Nagamichi (14th lord of Kuroda clan and Marquis), who grew up in this residence. He later became a noted ornithologist and a pioneer of protecting wild birds, animals and fish.

Marquis Kuroda had garden parties at his castle, and all former retainers and their families were invited. Parties were always on a grand scale; hundreds of people attended and renewed old friendships.

One autumn day in 1934, the Yonezawas attended the customary garden party. The garden looked colorful, with beautiful foliage. Magnificent bonsai and meticulously shaped chrysanthemums were decorated everywhere. Many venders supplied abundant food; sushi, chicken skewers, sandwiches, hors d' oeuvres, cakes, Japanese sweets and so on were prepared under several tents. All varieties of drinks: sake, wine, beer, juice, cider, tea and coffee were offered by servants. There were entertainers such as a magician and an amezaiku artist (Japanese candy craft artistry to make cute and realistic sculpture with multicolored taffy). A beautiful stage was set for music and dance.

Everyone enjoyed talking with friends and meeting new people. The party also worked as a great opportunity for social networking. While adults were dressed in formal kimono or western clothes, it was a rule that children wore their school uniforms. Yukiko was wearing the Futaba Women's School's uniform: a navy blue sailor-collared top with a pleated skirt. The sophisticated uniform with black lines and red anchor embroidery on the collar with black silk scarf was designed by a French designer and was a popular uniform. Yukiko saw a girl in the same uniform and noticed she was a classmate.

"Sayoko-san! Sayoko-san! Hello," Yukiko called.

"Oh, Yukiko-san. What a coincidence! Were your ancestors also retainers of the Kuroda clan?" Sayoko turned around and her eyes popped with astonishment.

"Yes. So, our ancestors worked for the same lords. Do you want to join us? My sisters and I are going to an amezaiku artist booth," Yukiko said.

"Sure. It's fun!"

Sayoko joined Yukiko, Kinuko, and Masako and they went to watch the amezaiku artist fashion small colorful sculptures with candy taffy. The artist was wearing a hanten (a traditional short coat) and a hair band. On her small desk were many candy samples in the shape of a bird or a dog, a monkey or a fox, a goldfish, a chrysanthemum and so on. As they watched, she picked up blob of hot green and white taffy, and transformed it into a dragon, shaped a dorsal fin with scissors, and painted red eyes and black beard: all within a few minutes.

"Wow!" the spectators exclaimed and gaped at the small candy dragon, that seemed almost ready to breathe fire.

She turned to Masako and asked her what she wanted. "Can you make a dog, a Shiba Inu? I have one at home. Light brown fur with a white stomach. She wears a red collar," said Masako.

"Sure" the artist said, and made a cute little dog with a perfectly curled tail, in 3 minutes.

"Thank you so much." Masako received the candy with great joy. Other girls had their candies made, such as a rabbit for Yukiko, a camellia for Kinuko, and a parrot for Sayoko.

"This is so pretty. I can't eat it," said Kinuko.

"I can't either," said the other girls.

"Let's save them for a while," said the girls. There were some wrapping papers on the desk, and the girls carefully wrapped the candies and held them.

The sound of shamisen filled with the atmosphere of Edo was heard from the stage and several geishas in black kimono with gorgeous designs on their skirts suddenly filled the proscenium. They were holding crimson maple branches in their hands and trailing long black kimonos. They danced elegantly, with traditional shamisen music and singing. With their hair done in Japanese coiffeur and graceful posture, they looked exactly like those beauties in the ukiyo-e wood block prints. Everyone was captivated by the scene.

The next performance was a famous male dance–the 'Kuroda Bushi'–performed by one of the former retainers. Kuroda Bushi is currently rendered as 'Kuroda song'. Before the war, it meant 'Koroda samurai', and is one of the most famous traditional folk songs in Japan. It had been sung by Kuroda samurai for a long time and the lyrics are about a true episode of the finest spear 'Nippon-go' and a samurai Mori Tahei Tomonobu.

The spear was originally owned by the Ogimachi emperor (1517-1593) and presented to the shogun Ashikaga Yoshiaki. It was given to the famous lord during the age of war–Oda Nobunaga, then passed to the Regent Toyotomi Hideyoshi; and finally, to a famous warrior–Fukushima Masanori.

One day, the Kuroda samurai, Mori Tahei Tomonobu, was invited to Fukushima Masanori's house.

This Tahei, it seemed, was a famous drinker, and lord Kuroda worried Tahei might cause trouble if he drank too much, and so enjoined him to refrain altogether at Masanori's house. Tahei kept his promise to the lord Kuroda and refused to drink. Finally, Masanori filled a huge cup and said. "If you finish up the sake in this huge cup, I will give you anything you want." After hearing this, Tahei chugged down the whole cup of sake and demanded the spear 'Nippon-go'.

It was a rule that a samurai never goes back on his word. Masanori had to give the spear to Tahei. Holding this spear proudly in his hand, Tahei went home singing an old folk song in Fukuoka (the original song of Kuroda Bushi). The spear, which is 3.2 meters and has an elegant relief of a dragon in the center groove of the blade, is now kept in the Fukuoka City Museum.

The Kuroda Bushi dance, performed with a long spear and a big sake cup, is very masculine. It has been sung and danced by everyone; however it had a very special meaning for the former retainers of the Kuroda clan.

While the performer started to dance with the solemn yet dynamic music, the audience gazed intensely. Tei, dressed in a light lavender kimono with a black and silver Hakata kenjo obi, was looking at the dance with a straight back.

Sayoko looked at her and whispered to Yukiko: "Your grandmother looks so elegant. Her short silver hair matches the lavender kimono."

"Only she can carry off such a hairstyle. Normally, old ladies put up their hair in traditional knots. I heard she was very beautiful when she was young," Yukiko said. Then, Kinuko added with a smile.

"And she was unladylike!"

"Yes, She still is unladylike," said Yukiko, and the girls giggled.

There was a funny episode about Tei. When they were living in Shibuya, a big fire broke out in a mansion near by. They were afraid that the fire might spread to their house.

Then Tei boldly said: "I will tie an okoshi (a long rectangular cloth wrapped around the body under kimono) to a saodake (a long bamboo stick used for drying clothes in the yard), and wave it to keep the fire away."

Yukiko's mother, Motoko said, "Mother, please don't do such an embarrassing thing."

But Tei didn't listen and said: "I have to stop the invading fire."

She continued waving the okoshi from the front yard of the house, which was on a slope above the burning mansion down the hill. The cloth was the size of a big flag. It sounds so funny, but Tei kept waving the big cloth so robustly. Amazingly, the fire retreated. The next day they saw a lady and her daughter come to the ruins of their house and collect something that had survived; they realized that Tei's house had been spared, because of her...unladylike behavior.

Tei, who was calm even when a fire broke out, had always been cautious. She taught her grandchildren how to escape if an earthquake hit and practiced that with them. The girls loved her very much. The calmness and bravery was in the typical spirit of a samurai's daughter.

This garden party was their last one; there were no more parties for the former Kuroda retainers and their families. A recession settled over Japan and the times became uneasy. Little by little, things had begun to change.

Hachiko Passes Away

After the statue of Hachiko was put up at Shibuya station on April 21st 1934, the dog sometimes sat and waited next to it. He looked very cute, if a bit puzzled–glancing up at his own statue. By this time, Hachiko had became so popular, that even people from far districts came all the way to Shibuya station to see him; and some even brought food.

But gradually, Hachiko began to grow weaker. He had been seriously ill twice before, but had miraculously recovered, thanks to dedicated care by the gardener, Kikusaburo, and the surrounding people. By early spring of 1935, it became hard for him to make the round trip between the station and Kikusaburo's house, and he often remained all day, at the station. People remarked that he spent more time lying on the floor.

On March 7th, a station employee noticed Hachiko frequenting several rooms in the station he normally didn't go to, and remaining in there for a while. He visited several shops near the station where sales-clerks were always kind to him. Then, he went back to his usual place—a wooden bed in front of the bag-gage room, and slept. Someone saw him still sleep-ing at the same place at 2 A.M on March 8th.

Around 6:00 A.M. on March 8th, a station employee came to work and found Hachiko was not sleeping in his usual place. He worriedly searched the station. He went outside but the plaza was empty. He called "Hachiko, Hachiko," and walked around. When he got near Inari bridge, he saw Hachiko lying on the side of the road. No one else was around. A gentle spring light shone on his big white body. The station employee called "Hachiko!" and touched the dog's body. It was still warm but there were no vital signs. It looked like Hachiko died just minutes earlier.

He returned to the station and informed the other employees of Hachiko's death. They moved his body to the luggage room and laid it on his bed. The news was relayed to Yaeko, Kikusaburo, Teru Ando (the sculptor) and several others. They hurried to the sta-tion, and gathered around Hachiko's body; a great heaviness in their hearts. Around 11 A.M., Yaeko wrapped Hachiko's statue in black and white rib-bons and offered flowers. In that way, everyone at the station—was made aware of Hachiko's passing.

The salesclerks in the shops told Yaeko and other people close to Hachiko that he had visited them all... the day before. They all wondered: Could he have known? A station employee suddenly realized why Hachiko had visited all the rooms of the station before his death... to offer reverence to the places that had sheltered and comforted him. These things were spoken of... and brought tears to people's eyes.

At Yukiko's school, shortly after Hachiko's death was officially made public at Shibuya, the news was released, and everyone grieved his death. Kinuko, Yukiko and several classmates stopped at Shibuya station on the way home, to mourn over Hachiko. When they arrived at the station, there were several thousand people gathered at the statue, offering flowers, fruits, sweets and letters. Cards. Telegrams.

Such an outpouring had seldom been seen in some people's lifetimes. A wake was held on the night of the 8th, and the station received callers for condolences until the 10th. On March 12th the memorial funeral was conducted at the small dog's shrine erected next to professor Ueno's grave. Aoyama cemetery: a large resting-place situated between Shibuya and Akasaka—a place famous for its abundant cherry trees, and its overwhelming sense of quietude... in the midst of Tokyo.

On the March 21st Vernal Equinox Day, the Yonezawas visited their ancestor's grave in Aoyama cemetery. It is Japanese custom to visit graves on the days of the Spring and Autumn Equinox, and during the Obon Festival.

"Come on, everyone, it's time to go" Ryusuke called to the family members.

Ryusuke, Motoko, Tei and all 5 children left the house and got into two taxis. Soon they arrived at the entrance of the cemetery. There were several traditional wooden houses that sold flowers and incense and lent wooden buckets and ladles for watering gravestones. Ryusuke and Motoko bought several flower bouquets and several bunches of incense. The incense for the dead consists of dozens of fine sticks, and one is supposed to present a set for a grave. The shop owner brought two wooden buckets and ladles. Ryusuke held one himself and told Takao to carry the other. The girls held flower bouquets and they walked to their ancestors' grave in the cemetery.

"These stones are huge," Sadao said, looking up the gravestones.

"They are flat slices of natural stones. They look very natural, don't they?" Ryusuke replied.

They poured water over the stones. When they finished the water in the buckets, Motoko had the boys run to the nearest faucet to refill them. After watering the stones, Ryusuke and Motoko lit incense. The refreshing smell of Japanese cedar drifted about. They offered flower bouquets to the gravestones and placed their palms together. After they finished, Tei asked: "Shall we visit Hachiko's grave? "

"Yes, please," replied the children.

"Professor Ueno's grave is a stone's throw away from here. Let's go.

I bought an extra bouquet and incense," Ryusuke said, and they started walking.

Professor Ueno's and Hachiko's graves were covered with many flowers. The dog's grave was marked with a small shrine with tiny steps. The children laid a bouquet for Hachiko and kneeled to pray. Ryusuke, Motoko and Tei also placed their palms together.

Tei said thoughtfully: "Isn't it interesting that we used to live so close to professor Ueno's house, and now...even the graves are close."

"I was thinking the same thing. There must be a special 'en' (ties originated in Buddhist philosophy), between Hachiko and us," replied Motoko.

"We can easily tarry at Hachiko's grave whenever we visit our ancestors'," Ryusuke answered.

The children gazed down at the little dog's shrine. Strangely, the same thought flitted through their minds: 'Finally Hachiko can greet his master again.' In the cemetery, the cherry blossoms were in full bloom. And the petals fell like snowflakes on the little shrine–petals of white... flecked with drops of red.

Turkish Ambassador

One day in March of 1936, two tall men were talking in the presidential room of the Dolmabahçe palace in Istanbul. Mustafa Kemal Atatürk, a handsome man with piercing gray eyes and a black suit was the founder and first President of the Turkish Republic. The other man, with blonde hair and wearing a dark blue suit, was Hüsrev Gerede. The palace was erected by Sultan Abdülmecid I in the middle of the 19th century, in an eclectic style of European Baroque and traditional Ottoman architecture. With the founding of the new nation, the palace's ownership was transferred to the national heritage site. The capital of Turkey was moved to Ankara and the official governing work has been transacted there since.

However, this palace has been used as the president's office in Istanbul and many important meetings were held here. The rooms were decorated in Baroque and Rococo style, with an abundance of gold and crystals. Its Bohemian and Baccarat crystal chandelier collection is the largest in the world. The palace is situated on the European shore of the Bosporus. A spectacular view of bright blue water glistening under sunlight—was visible through the big windows of the room.

"Have the preparation for your move to Japan been completed? " asked the President.

"Yes," Hüsrev replied. He was appointed ambassador to Japan and would travel there within a week.

"How is the plan for the erection of the Ertuğrul monument?"

"We've been working on it with the cooperation of the Turkish embassy in Tokyo, and it has progressed as planned. We will erect the monument designed by the Turkish architect and will conduct the 50th anniversary ceremony with the completion ceremony next year. The actual 50th anniversary would be in 1939. However, we think it would be ideal to hold this large memorial at the time of the completion of the new monument. I am honored to be in charge of the project," replied Hüsrev.

"I admire the Meiji Emperor. This will be a very meaningful project. I also appreciated the royal visit of the Showa Emperor to the Kashinozaki Ertuğrul incident site in 1929. Please give my best to the Showa emperor," Atatürk said.

"I duly will. We are planning to conduct the memorial ceremony on the day of the Showa emperor's visit, which will be on June 3rd," replied Hüsrev.

"Very good," president Atatürk said, and smiled.

Hüsrev Gerede was one of the 18 generals of Atatürk when he led the landing at Samsun–the Black Sea port on 19th May of 1919, which was the beginning of the Turkish war of independence. The two were war-comrades in a difficult time and had been very close since.

There were exchanges between the Edo Shoguns and the Ottoman Empire, such as the presentations of treasures, though the real exchange was started by the Ertuğrul incident. The friendship of the two countries deepened rapidly afterwards. Accordingly, the Ertuğrul incident has had a special meaning for the two countries.

***

Ryusuke, Jo Iimura, Zeki Bayat, and Koji Okubo were sitting in the living room of Ryusuke's house. Takao, then 9 years old, was sitting next to Ryusuke. Many pictures were laid out on a table.

"Please allow Takao to sit with us. He wants to see the pictures. He likes cameras and taking pictures," said Ryusuke.

"Of course. This is not an official meeting," said Jo, and looked at the boy with a warm smile.

"Takao-kun (kun is a friendly suffix to add to call a boy or young man), these are the pictures of Kashinozaki lighthouse and the ocean. There are so many interesting looking rocks, but the ocean is very rough," Zeki added, while showing pictures to Takao.

"Wow, the cliff looks so steep!" he exclaimed.

"You are correct. Therefore, it was extremely difficult for the fishermen to carry the injured Turkish officers and sailors to the top. Especially, on a pitch-dark stormy night," Ryusuke explained.

"I can imagine. I was thinking maybe they climbed up steps. But they carried the people on such a precipice!" Takao said while looking at the pictures.

There were several pictures of the gravestone for the lost, which was built with donations, after the incident. The epitaph on this gravestone will be mounted on a new monument. The adults were talking and sometimes they used the word 'teiso'.

Finally, Takao asked: "What is teiso?"

"Good question, Takao-kun. Teiso refers to the laying of the foundation stone, or to the stone itself. To build a castle, a temple or a house, the most important thing is to lay down a good foundation. Therefore, when you build something, you put an important foundation stone in, and conducts a ceremony. It seems they have the same custom all over the world.

In Europe it is called a cornerstone laying ceremony," answered Jo.

"Yes, and people carve information on the stone, such as who built it, when, why, for what purpose. Also, people put records; for instance, blueprints, the newspaper of the time, the name of the people who built it, in a metal box, and bury it under the foundation stone," Ryusuke answered.

"Interesting! So that is teiso," Takao remarked as he tried to remember the word.

"If the stone is buried under the monument, no one will be able to see it, will they? " asked Takao.

"No, unless someone in the future decides to reconstruct the building from the foundation. Which normally won't happen for decades or centuries. However, this way, someone in the future would know about the building if they needed to do something with it," answered Ryusuke.

"Takao-kun, it is a time capsule. Normally no one will open it for a long time, but those who open a teiso box in the far away future would find vivid information of the time it was buried," explained Koji.

"Wow, that is amazing. What will you do with the teiso of the Ertuğrul monument? " Takao asked.

"That is what we are discussing. Soon, the new ambassador will arrive at his post in Tokyo and we will decide with him," answered Ryusuke.

***

In late March, Hüsrev Gerede, the Turkish ambassador to Japan, arrived in Tokyo. Ryusuke started to work with him and other staff of the embassy, on the Ertuğrul monument project. He often talked about it at home and naturally the children learned about the Ertuğrul incident and the progress of the project. At the same time, Ryusuke and Zeki were working on their Turkish conversation book, outside the office. It took time, but started to bear fruit little by little.

On a beautiful Sunday in May, they were invited to the ambassador's residence. Ryusuke wore a suit, Motoko, and the three girls in kimonos, and the boys in stand-up collar school uniforms—all came out from the house. When they walked down the steps to the street, a neighbor was passing by and said.

"Oh, you are all dressed up. Where are you heading?"

"We are invited to the Turkish ambassador's house for afternoon tea," joyfully replied Ryusuke.

The neighbor commented: "The girls are wearing furisode! (a long sleeve formal kimono worn by young girls before they marry) They look so pretty!"

"Usually, they like to wear dresses. However, we thought it would be nice to wear kimonos today," Motoko answered.

"It's joyful to see the girls in their colorful furisode. It's eye-popping for me too," the neighbor said and smiled.

At this time, the girls were 16, 14, and 12 years old. All furisode were dyed in patterns with bright colors such as orange, purple, green, blue and yellow, and accented with embroidery and gold leaf. On these furisode, they wore flamboyant obi sashes tied in bow knots in back, with ribbons in their hair.

The ambassador's house was in Shoto, Shibuya, near where they used to live. They took the streetcar to Shibuya station and walked up a slope to the residence. The ambassador's house was an English Tudor style mansion with a large garden. For the children it was like traveling to a foreign country.

Hüsrev Gerede was a tall and lean handsome man. His wife was very pretty and looked like an actress in an elegant dress. The room was decorated attractively in a European taste.

"Konnichiwa, Yokoso (Good afternoon, welcome)," the ambassador and Mrs. Gerede said in Japanese with a smile. "Merhaba. Elçi Gerede, Nasilsiniz? (Good afternoon, Ambassador Gerede, how are you?)" the children greeted him in Turkish. The ambassador and Mrs. Gerede praised Motoko and the girls' kimono. They continued talking in Turkish, and afterwards in French. Rüştü and his wife Nimet were also invited. They spoke Japanese, and thus, the conversation sometimes switched to Japanese, and Rüştü translated it for the ambassador and Mrs. Gerede.

The table was covered by white linen with gorgeous handmade lace, which was a traditional Turkish textile. Matching linen napkins were set and colorful tulip flowers arranged in a silver base with elaborate emboss on the center of the table. Tea and coffee were served in blue arabesque pattern cups and saucers. Cookies and fruit jellies, crème puffs, locum (Turkish delight) and baklava–beckoned from silver trays. Those Turkish desserts–made with gel, sugar or layers of fillo filled with pistachio, apricot, hazel nuts, dates, and honey–were very rare in Japan, and the Yonezawas appreciated the delicacies. While having tea and desserts, they enjoyed chatting about the affairs of the day–some light; some, more pressing.

One Turkish servant, a girl of 17, had learned a Japanese song. Urged by the ambassador to sing, the girl stood in front of everybody bashfully. When she started to sing a song by Yoshie Fujiwara (a very popular tenor at the time), everyone was amazed by her beautiful voice and perfect Japanese pronunciation. The guests were impressed and applauded. It added to a wonderful afternoon.

After the event, the girls often tried to duplicate the afternoon tea at the Turkish ambassador's house. They searched for things they could use for the tea, such as lace, china, a tray, and desserts; then arranged them nicely and enjoyed cute tea parties at home.

One day, Ryusuke came home and told them at the dinner table that there was an interesting visitor at the embassy.

"This gentleman, Mr. Bruno Taut, is a famous German architect and has been living in Takasaki, in Gunma, since 1933. He is a political exile and has published books on Japanese architecture. He will be moving to Turkey soon."

"Why is that?" Motoko asked.

"He worked there before, to build the German-Turkey friendship house. Since then he has been interested in the country. This time he was offered a post as the Turkish government's main architect from president Atatürk," Ryusuke answered.

"Wow, that sounds like a big post," Motoko said.

"Yes. He said he has also been asked to be director of the Istanbul Art Academy. He will design institutional buildings in Istanbul and Ankara. By the way, he said he also saw Hachiko when the dog was alive," said Ryusuke.

"I see. Zeki-san told me Hachiko was famous among the foreign community in Japan as well," Motoko said.

"Mr. Taut said he was deeply moved by the fact that the statue was erected while the dog was still alive," Ryusuke said.

"Maybe for an artist it was interesting to see the model and the artwork sitting together," Motoko said with a smile.

"I think so. Sometimes Hachiko sat exactly in the same pose as the statue. Do you remember? " Yukiko said, and looked at the other children.

"I remember that. They were like twins! One time, Hachiko looked up at his own statue and seemed to smile," Masako said.

"Oh, I remember, he was so cute," the girls said unanimously.

***

In October 1936, Ryusuke accompanied ambassador Gerede and visited Kyoto and Kushimoto in Wakayama, with the other embassy staff. First, ambassador Gerede made an official visit to the Momoyama Imperial Mausoleum (the mausoleum for the Emperor Meiji) in Fushimi, Kyoto.

Next, the party visited the Kashinozaki Erutuğrul memorial site and conducted the cornerstone laying ceremony. After a traditional Shinto ceremony in the presence of the people of Wakayama and the party, ambassador Gerede laid the first stone at the construction site.

After the ceremony, ambassador Gerede met some of those who saved the Turkish people in 1890. Most were in their 70s, as 47 years had passed since the incident. While listening to their stories, the ambassador was overcome by emotion and took the hand of the elder, Takichi Yamamoto, saying "This is the highest way to show respect in Turkey," and kissed his hand and wept. The surrounding people were surprised by his heartfelt act.

Rüştü said to Ryusuke: "This is the first time we have seen the ambassador—a war veteran—weep," Nobody could contain themselves and they all wept.

The ceremony and meeting ended successfully. The ambassador and the party agreed to the next meeting, which would be the unveiling ceremony of the monument with the people of Kushimoto. A wonderful feeling of friendship swept over everyone.

Ertuğrul Monument Unveiling Ceremony

On a beautiful clear day, June 3rd of 1937, the unveiling ceremony of the Ertuğrul monument was conducted. The party from the Turkish embassy and other attendees from Tokyo traveled by train and by the Naval cruiser Oi. They transferred to a small boat while off shore, which took them to Kashinozaki wharf. Hundreds of villagers met the party at the wharf. From the wharf to the monument was about a 15-minute drive. There were many welcome arches on the road–and villagers on the roadside waved the flags of Turkey and Japan. About 5000 people gathered for the event.

Figure 13: Ambassador Gerede in front of the Ertuğrul monument at the 50th memorial ceremony in 1937.

The monument was a 12.75 meter tower with a pyra-mid shaped top, and the epitaph from the first grave-stone was mounted in the center. Ambassador Gere-de pulled the cord of a white cloth and unveiled a tall gray stone monument. A Shinto priest conducted a ceremony and representatives from Turkey and Japan offered sprigs from sacred trees.

After speeches by honorable guests, rice cakes wrapped in paper–were then scattered, to mark the completion of the building. It was a cheerful event after a solemn ceremony. The governor of Wakayama, ambassador Gerede, and several other people quickly climbed on top of the stage and threw hundreds of rice cakes. The crowd laughed, ran around and caught the rice cakes. Following the rice cake throwing was a banquet dinner of grand scale, served under a large tent. The general public, along with the parties concerned with the event, were invited. After the dinner, ambassador Gerede and the officers of Oi distributed goody bags to all the children.

Ryusuke, Zeki, Rüstü and all other people who prepared the event were so glad it turned out a huge success. It was a memorial service, and at the same time, a wonderful harbinger of future friendship.

As the cruiser Oi pulled away from Kashinozaki wharf, thousands of villagers on the shore shouted loudly "Banzai, Turkey," to which the party on the Oi replied back "Banzai, Nippon," and then sounded a whistle. Ryusuke and Zeki looked at each other and smiled.

Helen Keller & Akita Dogs

*O*n the afternoon of July of 1937, Yukiko and Masako were sitting in the living room and looking at girls' magazines. The magazines had color pictures and beautiful illustrations by famous artists. One magazine included fashion articles by a Japanese artist living in Paris. The girls loved to read his articles, with its sophisticated illustrations.

They heard Kinuko's voice from the front entrance. She closed the door and rushed into the house saying, "I'm home. Mom, Yukiko, Masako, where are you?" Then, she noticed that Yukiko and Masako were in the living room and came in.

***

Kinuko graduated from the girl's school the previous spring and was now a student at Tsuda college.

Tsuda college was founded by Umeko Tsuda, who studied in the US from 1872 to 1882 and 1889 to 1892. She was sent to the US as the youngest member (6 years old) of the Meiji government diplomatic mission, and became an educator and a pioneer in education for women. The college is famous for its excellent English educational program.

"Guess who is coming to our school tomorrow?" Kinuko exclaimed.

"What? Is someone very famous coming to Tsuda college?" asked Yukiko curiously.

"Yes. A world famous woman from America!" Kinuko answered.

"Shirley Temple!" Masako said.

"No. But just as famous," answered Kinuko.

"Oh, then Helen Keller, I guess," said Yukiko.

"Right. Right. Helen Keller will come to our school and make a speech," Kinuko said proudly.

"Wow, I wish I could go," Yukiko and Masako said unanimously.

Helen Keller was very famous in Japan. Everyone was moved by her effort and determination to overcome the adversity of being blind and deaf, to become a leading humanitarian. People admired her enthusiastically and she was regarded almost as a saint. The news that Kinuko would actually meet her was amazing for Yukiko and Masako.

On the next day, after Kinuko came back from the college, everyone gathered around her and heard about Helen Keller's visit.

"We were all so impressed. She gave us a speech through her hand sign language. Then Ms. Thomson, her assistant, translated it into English, which was translated into Japanese by our principal. There were some talented students who could understand the English speech by Ms. Thomson," explained Kinuko. Then, she added an interesting story. "Ms. Keller said her mother told her about the Japanese blind scholar of the Edo era, Hanawa Hokiichi, and that she should use him as a role-model. We were surprised that she knew about someone from the Edo era."

"It is interesting. There is a museum for Hanawa Hokiichi's achievement in Shibuya. I learned that Mr. Hanawa learned Chinese characters through a monk who taught him how to write on his palm," Motoko said.

"Ms. Keller visited the museum. She told us that she was very happy, and was honored that she could visit the museum. She touched the statue of Mr. Hanawa and his original desk."

"That is indeed great," Motoko said.

Kinuko then added other exciting piece of news she had heard. "Ms. Keller visited the statue of Hachiko and ran her hand across it several times. She said she was so impressed by his faithfulness and always wanted to visit the statue. She is also traveling to

Akita –where Hachiko was from. She said she would like to have an Akita dog and take it back to America."

"I'm sure an Akita would be a wonderful companion for Ms. Keller," Ryusuke said.

Figure 14: Helen Keller with the Akita dog Kenzan-go, circa 1939.

A few days later, Helen Keller traveled to Akita and gave a speech entitled 'Through the Darkness and Silence,' in front of more than 2000 people, at the Akita prefectural meeting hall. On this visit, she asked if there was an Akita dog that she could adopt. She keeps dogs from America, England, Germany and France–at her Connecticut home. She said she could feel the atmosphere of the countries by touching and living with these dogs. She was so moved by Hachi-ko and she wants to keep an Akita dog. She said it would deepen ties between Japan and the US.

After hearing of her love for the animal, Ichiro Ogas-awara, a young police officer from the town of Odate where Hachiko was from, and who was also a master in the art of Kendo, offered to give Ms. Keller his 75 day old Akita puppy 'Kamikaze-go' (the word 'kami-kaze' originally meant 'divine wind', which is a Shin-to word. During the second world war, the airplanes for the Tokko-tai, Special Attack Unit, whose mis-sion was suicide attacks, were named kamikaze and this meaning spread around the world. 'go' is a suffix commonly used for trains, cars, airplanes, ships and dogs–typically for working dogs)

The cute puppy, Kamikaze, returned to America with Helen Keller. He was the very first Akita dog in-troduced in America. Helen and Kamikaze got along very well. Unfortunately, he died of canine distem-per after two months. Helen was very upset.

Ichiro Ogasawara heard of her sorrow and decided to present Kamikaze's elder brother 'Kenzan-go' to Ms. Keller. In 1939, Kenzan traveled to New York by ocean liner and was received by Helen Keller. Kenzan spent long years in her home in Westport Connecticut. Hachiko's lofty spirit was succeeded by two Akita dogs brought back to America by Helen

Keller, and since then, the breed has become known all over the world.

Helen Keller sent several letters to Ichiro Ogas-awara. In her letter to him on the 20th of November, 1937 she wrote as follows:

If ever there was an angel in fur, it was Kamikaze.

1938

*T*he Turkish conversation book Ryusuke and Zeki had worked on for years was finally published in July of 1938. Its title was 'Türkçe-Japonca Muhavere Kitabı' (Turkish-Japanese Conversation Book). On the red silk cover the title was printed in gold letters in both Turkish and Japanese. The volume contained of a dictionary, useful expressions, examples of conversation and grammar. It was published by Sansaisha, a publishing company known for books related to France. They chose red for the cover as it was the color for both Turkish and Japanese flags.

In the book is a congratulatory address by ambassador Hüsrev Gerede and a preface by general Jo Iimura. Following these is an introduction by Ryusuke Yonezawa. Ryusuke and Zeki were pleased that the books would also be shipped to Turkey for many people to use.

Another event that happened in 1938 was the completion of the Tokyo Mosque in Shibuya. Several hundred Tatar exiles were hoping to build a mosque and eventually it was realized. The beautiful mosque consisted of a dome and three layered minaret surrounded with palm trees; adding an exotic atmosphere to the area. While Japanese people enthusiastically started to adopt western architecture from the 1920s, Islamic design was also introduced. It had become quite popular for western style mansions to build Islamic design cigar rooms and arabesque tile bathrooms. Therefore, the people living in the area accepted this exotic addition to their neighborhood quite favorably.

On the 10th of November in 1938, president Kemal Atatürk of Turkey suddenly passed away at the Dolmabahçe palace while at work. It was terribly sad news for Ryusuke and all the staff of the Turkish embassy. They wished they could work more for the president. Though, they were saved just by the accomplishment of the Ertuğrul monument, while he was alive. It was the president's earnest request.

Meanwhile, Yukiko and the children were too young to understand what was going on in the world; however they overheard the adults' conversation about the war between Japan and China, which started in 1937. As a result of this, the growing opinion to cancel the Tokyo Olympics was heard domestically as well as abroad. The final decision to cancel it was made in July of 1938.

Figure 15: Noel Nouet's ukiyoe print, Inokashira park, 1936.

Zeki Bayat was ordered to leave Japan in December. It was unfortunate for both Zeki and Ryusuke; but they were happy they could complete two important things together; erection of the Ertuğrul monument and publication of the book.

One day in early December, the Yonezawas invited Zeki to their house for a farewell dinner. Zeki had already had a formal farewell party at the embassy. This was a casual dinner with the family and the foreign students staying at their house. They prepared several low tables laid together with floor cushions in a Japanese room for a sukiyaki dinner. This way, over 10 people could sit together. It was getting cold in Tokyo in December, and a warm sukiyaki dinner cooked right on the table was perfect. Everyone enjoyed the dinner and conversation.

After dinner, Zeki went outside in the garden with the children and offered some food to Yildiz, the dog he gave them several years before. Yildiz had taken to Zeki as he often visited Ryusuke's house. Zeki patted her gently and said good-by to the Shiba-Inu. The dog he kept would be adopted by the landlord of the house Zeki rented, as it got along well with the family.

While Zeki and the children were outside in the yard, Motoko, Tei and Kiyo prepared tea and coffee in the living room. When Zeki and the children came into the living room, Ryusuke and Motoko held up a flat package and said.

"Zeki-san, here is a present for you from us."

"Oh, thank you very much," Zeki answered.

"Please open it," Motoko said with a smile. Zeki sat on a sofa, opened the package and found a set of beautiful wood block prints made by Noel Nouet 'Scenes of Tokyo, Twenty-four views'.

"Wow, these are for me? These are so beautiful. Thank you very much. I will remember my days in Tokyo whenever I see them," said Zeki delightedly.

"These are the places you know very well. Look, this is the Sakurada gate, this is Ueno park, Asakusa temple...," Ryusuke explained while spreading the prints on a table.

"Noel-san is really talented. There is something very poetic about his art works," Zeki said while looking at the prints.

"Perhaps because he is also a poet," Motoko said. Tei looked on with a smile.

"They look very nice to me. I always thought wood-block prints were only good for Edo scenery. To the contrary, the scenes of the western building by a moat and a European bridge of Nihonbashi look beautiful in Noel-san's prints."

"Yes, indeed, I look forward to showing these to my family and friends," Zeki said. Then he took a box and put it on the table.

"This is a present from me to you. Please open the box."

Ryusuke opened the box and found an intricately hand–engraved copper plate.

"Oh, this is wonderful. What elaborate engraving! Thank you very much Zeki-san." Ryusuke said.

"This will look great on the wall in this room, won't it? Thank you so much. We will treasure it," Motoko said.

Aya Sophia was engraved in the center of the plate— surrounded by a sophisticated arabesque design. The children came to the table and admired the plate.

Zeki and the Yonezawas were so absorbed in their conversation that they forgot the passing of the time.

Departure

On the 12th of December of 1938, Zeki left Yo-kohama on a European passenger liner 'Ha-runa-maru' for Istanbul. Ryusuke, Yukiko and Yukiko's school friend Mitsuko, whose father also worked for the Turkish embassy, went to the port in Yokohama to see Zeki Bayat off.

It was a clear winter day and the magnificent figure of Mt. Fuji was seen beyond the ocean against a deep blue sky, in the background. The top of Mt. Fuji was covered with snow and contrast of the mountain's grayish blue and pure white top was spectacular. 'Haruna-maru' was a 187-meter-long ship, with two masts and a big funnel. It was standing tall in front of the wharf. There were many small boats moving back and forth, to deliver luggage and containers to the ship.

"This is a gorgeous ship. This one will travel all the way to Europe, right? " Yukiko asked Ryusuke.

"Yes. 'Haruna-maru' is a famous European liner. It will stop at ports like Shanghai and Singapore; Colombo, Bombay, Aden; pass through the Suez Canal, then on to Istanbul. Zeki-san will get off the ship there. But she will cruise to several ports in Europe. Professor Albert Einstein traveled on this ship when he visited Japan."

"Really? I can't wait to see the inside," Yukiko answered.

The three ascended the gangway ladder and boarded the ship. Then they asked a crew member where Zeki's room was. He guided them to a lounge where a grand staircase lead to the upper levels. They walked up the grand staircase and then another stairway to a hallway in the first class cabin floor. From the big window in the hallway, they found Zeki standing on the upper deck and looking at the scenery. They walked outside to the deck.

"Good morning, Zeki-san. What a serene day for a voyage," Ryusuke said.

"Good morning, Ryusuke-san, Yukiko-san and Mitsuko-san. Thank you very much for coming all the way to Yokohama to see me off. It surely is a beautiful day. I'm so lucky to see such a great view of Mt. Fuji," answered Zeki.

"There are many noted vantage points for scenic views of Mt. Fuji. However, this is spectacular.

Standing on a high deck and finding Mt. Fuji right in front staring back at you is... breathtaking." Ryusuke said with admiration.

The four talked for a while on the deck and Ryusuke spoke to the girls.

"Zeki-san and I need to talk in his cabin. How about you two look around the ship and meet us at a café lounge over there in about an hour? You may order anything you want at the café."

"Sure. We would love to explore the ship," Yukiko and Mitsuko said with smiles and left.

The interior of the ship was an eclectic style of Art Deco and the oriental. Large lacquer paintings of a wisteria tree, a five storied pagoda, koi fish in a pond, ladies in kimono and so on decorated the walls. Chairs and sofas were upholstered with Art Deco textiles, and modern lighting illuminated the space cheerfully. Tropical palm trees in big pots were placed everywhere. The passengers of the ship were from many countries and several foreign languages were heard.

"Look at that lady. She's so fashionable," Mitsu-ko said while admiring a foreign lady in an orange, black and white geometrical pattern dress with a black belt and a black hat."

"Wow, she looks right out of Vogue magazine," Yuki-ko said.

The girls enjoyed going over the passengers' chic fashions. After strolling around the ship, they sat at a table in the café and ordered juice. Zeki and Ryusuke came back to the café and sat with them.

"Yukiko-san and Mitsuko-san, here are official pamphlets of the 'Haruna-maru'," Zeki said as he handed them colorful booklets.

"Thank you very much," they said and turned the pages of the booklets.

"Oh, look at these. Pictures of Aya Sophia, Topkapi Palace, the Blue mosque, and Cappadocia! What incredible scenery," Yukiko said with astonishment.

"There are so many interesting places in Turkey. When you grow up, please visit my country," Zeki said with a smile.

"Yes! I would love to. Mitsuko-san, let's visit Turkey together," Yukiko said.

"That is a good idea! Let's do it! " Mitsuko answered cheerfully.

"Meanwhile, let's exchange letters. Please write to me in Turkish," Zeki said.

"Yes, I will. But I can't write Turkish very well," said Yukiko.

"Use the book your father and I made," Zeki said with a smile.

"Yes, you should. Why not? Zeki-san, maybe you will find some exact same sentences from our book in their letters," Ryusuke said with laughter.

"Maybe!" said the girls and everyone started to laugh.

This helped to distract them from the sadness of parting.

Finally, it was time to say goodbye. Ryusuke, Yukiko and Mitsuko had firm handshakes with Zeki, saying "Good bye, have a wonderful trip," and descended from the ship.

From the deck, a crew member sounded a gong. Hundreds of people present for the send-off looked up at the ship. The passengers on the deck began to throw paper tapes. The people on the wharf grabbed the ends, and hundreds of colorful tapes formed a temporary bridge between the ship and the shore. The entangled fine tapes fluttered about in the wind.

Ryusuke, Yukiko and Mitsuko searched for Zeki.

"Oh, there he is," Ryusuke pointed. Zeki was tall and easy to find among the crowd. He was holding a tape, waving his hand and saying goodbye with a big smile.

"Yes, I can see him," the girls said.

"Goodbye Zeki-san! Ogenkide (Stay well)! " Yukiko said while waving her hand as hard as she could.

The ship sounded a long whistle and sloughed its moorings. Hundreds of colorful tapes became longer and longer until finally they broke and fell in the ocean. On that instant, the tapes swirled like ephemeral fireworks. The temporary bridge disappeared. The white liner sailed away, fluttering the long paper tapes gently in the air.

Reminiscence of the past years came to Ryusuke's mind like a phantasmagoria. Zeki, shooting a Japanese bow and arrow under the blooming cherry trees, meetings lasting through the nights at the embassy, rejoicing over the completion of the Ertuğrul monument... chatting and laughing in Ryusuke's garden with Aka and Yildiz running around.

The 'Haruna-maru' glided slowly off, into the shining sea. The ship grew smaller, trailing along white wake behind it.... Ryusuke, Yukiko and Mitsuko were glancing at the ship standing still until it finally disappeared over the horizon.

Epilogue

Colonel Ryusuke Yonezawa was placed on the reserve list but recalled to active service as an official interpreter in French Indochina and Singapore. He was killed in an airplane crash in the Malacca Straits, on the way to Borneo in 1943.

Zeki Bayat went back to the Turkish Navy.

Ambassador Hüsrev Gerede was appointed Ambassador to Germany in 1939 and moved to Berlin.

Marquis Maeda, also known as General Toshinari Maeda, was placed on the reserve list, but recalled to active service as a commander in Borneo, and died in an airplane crash off the Borneo coast in 1942.

Koji Okubo's 'Institute for Islamic Area Studies' (Kaikyo-ken Kenkyujo) was lost in a Tokyo air raid, with his collection of 10,000 books. The Tatar refugees collected money and bought a house for him as a reward for his kindness.

Noel Nouet stayed in Tokyo and then Karuizawa during the war. He came back to Tokyo in the fall of 1945 and started to teach French at universities and schools.

The Statue of Hachiko was delivered to the army for scrap metal in 1944. The sculptor of the original statue, Teru Ando, was killed in a Tokyo air raid. After the war, the American military asked Tokyo officials the whereabouts of the statue of Hachiko. They demanded the statue be rebuilt, and said if the Japanese couldn't do it, the US would. Interested persons in Shibuya decided to rebuild it, and asked Teru Ando's son Takeshi, who was also a sculptor, to make it. The current statue of Hachiko was unveiled on August 15th, 1948. It is called 'Chuken Hachiko' (loyal dog Hachiko) as before.

The 'Turkish-Japanese Conversation Book' (Türkçe-Japonca, Muhavere Kitabı) that Ryusuke and Zeki published in 1938 was lost from the Yonezawa house as a result of the Tokyo air raid. However, in 2008 I found the book, kept in several libraries as follows: Tokyo Kogakuin University, the National Diet Library, the Japan Foundation, Hokkaido University, Musashi University and Rikkyo University. I also found a reprinted version of the book at an antique bookshop in Istanbul in 2012. The guide who helped me to find the book bought the book and presented it to me. I felt the past and the present merged. Now I keep it on my bookshelf.

In 2008, I met a person who had been keeping an old leather bound business card folder which was given to her by a Turkish man whose relatives had lived in Japan long time ago. I found that the folder belonged to Zeki Bayat, by the post card inside, which bears his name and address and the names of officers on the cards kept inside. The folder was in mint condition, and frozen in time... 1938.

In 2012, I visited Hüsrev Gerede's statue in Nişantaşi in Istanbul where he used to live. The lady who had been living in this elegant neighborhood more than 70 years told me, in the old days residents spoke to each other in mixed French and Turkish. In two far away places; Shibuya in Tokyo and Nişantaşi in Istanbul, the same lifestyle once existed.

I visited the Ertuğrul monument in Kushimoto, Wakayama in June of 2012. The municipal employee who helped with my research found the documentary film of the 1937 Ertuğrul monument unveiling and the 50th memorial ceremony at archives of the Kushimoto town office. The film brought back vivid scenes of the ceremony after 75 years.

Acknowledgement

*F*irstly, I want to thank my grandfather Ryusuke Yonezawa for leaving beautiful photos of the 1930s, and his Turkish-Japanese conversation book 'Türkçe-Japonca Muhavere Kitabı' . I want to thank my mother Yukiko Hosono for telling me of all these interesting stories. I want to thank my brother, Satoshi Hosono, my aunt Masako Karube, my uncle Takao Yonezawa and my cousin Kyoko Sawaguchi for helping me find old facts.

I would like to thank the following people; my husband, James McDonald for proof reading my manuscript, my son George for suggestions and my daughter Alice for drawing Hachiko's silhouette and illustration. Keita Matsui of Shibuya Folk and Literary Shirane Memorial Museum for lending me old pictures and helping me with my research on Hachiko. Norihiko Wakutani from the Kushimoto Town Office for helping with my research on the Ertugrül monument, Yuko Omagari of the Japan-Turkey Society for letting me use their library materials, Helen Selsdon of the American Foundation for the Blind for showing important documents concerning and written by Helen Keller and Pinar Gokpinar for proof reading my writings on Turkey.

I want to extend my sincere gratitude to the editor, Dr. Steven Darian for editing my manuscript and giving me wonderful advice.

Thank you very much to the publisher, Jay Herath of Linus Books for their marvelous job in making this book.

Glossary

Akita ken/Akita Inu

Akita Ken/Akita Inu is a breed of dog from Akita in northern Japan.

Benten

Benten/Benzaiten is a Japanese Shinto and Buddhism mixed goddess, who originated from the Hindu goddess Sarasvati. Benten is usually enshrined at a location near water such as a pond, sea, river or a fountain.

Chashitsu

Tea room or tea house built specifically for the purpose of conducting tea ceremonies.

Chonmage

The chonmage is a hairstyle worn by samurai in the Edo period. The hair on the forehead and crown is shaved and the remaining hair is tied into a topknot.

Edo period

The Edo period (1603-1868) was the period when the Tokugawa shogunate ruled Japan. Its capital city was called Edo, now Tokyo.

En

Bond, ties, fate-originated in Buddhism philosophy.

Engawa

A wooden corridor built outside of a tatami mat room in a house. Sometimes it also refers to a wooden veranda built outside of a house.

Furisode

A type of formal kimono with extremely long sleeves (2.8'-3.8') worn by young unmarried women.

Futon

Traditional Japanese bedding which consists of a mattress and a cover, used in Japanese tatami mat rooms. They are stored in closets when not in use.

Hakama

Hakama are a type of Japanese traditional trousers worn especially by men (occasionally women wear hakama as well) for formal occasions and for performing traditional martial arts such as kendo, iaido, aikido, and kyudo.

Ise Shrine

The Ise Shrine (Ise Jingu), also called the Grand Shrine of Ise, is located in the city of Ise in Mie prefecture. It is a very important and sacred Shinto shrine complex and a popular place of pilgrimage.

Kabuki

Traditional Japanese dance-drama performed only by male actors with elaborate make-up and colorful costumes.

Kamishimo

Kamishimo is a traditional formal outfit which consists of a vest with exaggerated shoulders and hakama (traditional wide trousers), worn during the Edo period.

Kimono

The Japanese traditional garment, a kimono is a straight-lined robe with long and wide sleeves, worn with a sash called obi.

Koinobori

Koinobori are carp-shaped wind socks that attach to a pole to flutter in the wind. These are flown on Children's Day, which is May 5th.

Kurobune (Kurofune)

Kurobune or Kurofune means black ship in Japanese. Mostly, it means the black ships (Mississippi, Plymouth, Saratoga, and Susquehana) that sailed into Tokyo Bay in 1853 and in 1854, led by the US Commodore Mathew Perry, who demanded that the Tokugawa shogunate to open the country to trade.

Meiji period

In 1868, the Tokugawa shogunate fell to the Meiji restoration. The Meiji period was named for the ruler, the Emperor Meiji and lasted until 1912. Japanese society changed from the Edo feudal society to a modern society.

Ooku

Ooku was the special area of a castle where the women connected to the reigning shogun and daimyo (lord) resided.

Odaiba

The original odaiba was a series of six artificial island fortresses constructed in 1853 in order to protect Edo. Later these islands were constantly expanded and now serve as a major commercial and residential area of Tokyo.

Otogizoushi

Otogizoushi refers to traditional story books, with illustrations published from the medieval period to the Edo period.

Roji

Japanese garden leading to a house or tea house (chashitsu). Mostly used in relation to tea ceremony, roji includes the stepping stones, a basin, moss, and bamboo gate.

Shamisen

Shamisen is a three stringed traditional musical instrument.

Shiba Inu

Shiba Inu is a small breed of Japanese dog that has a fox-like face.

Shoji

Shoji is a sliding room divider or window consisting of translucent paper over a frame of a lattice wood.

Showa period

The Showa period was the period during the reign of the Showa Emperor, from 1926 to 1989.

Taisho period

The Taisho period was from 1912 to 1926, during the reign of the Emperor Taisho.

Tatami

A tatami is a type of mat made of rice straw for use in Japanese rooms.

Tokiwazu

A style of narrative music and singing that was used in kabuki theater for dance and dance plays.

Toshogu- shrine

A Toshogu-shrine is a Shinto shrine in which Tokugawa Ieyasu, the first shogun of the Tokugawa shogunate, is enshrined.

Tsuzura

A traditional bamboo box coated with lacquer

Ukiyo-e

Ukiyo-e are woodblock prints that were made in the 17th to the 19th century in Japan.

Reference Materials

A newspaper article, The death of the Akita Dog Ka-mimaze-go, Sad News from Helen Keller, Akita: Aki-ta Sakigake Shinpo, 12/24/1937

A. J. Watts, Japanese Warships of World War, New York: Doubleday & Company Inc., 1973

Hachiko Exhibition Catalog, Tokyo: Shibuya Folk and Literary Shirane Memorial Museum, 2013

Kaikyo-ken (Islamic Area), Tokyo: Institute for Islamic Area Studies, 1939

Kunio Nishina, Inu no Isemairi (Dog's Pilgrimage to Ise Shrine), Tokyo: Heibonsha, 2013

Modern and Contemporary Shibuya Seen Through Architecture, Tokyo: Shibuya Folk and Literary Shi-rane Memorial Museum, 2007

Noel Nourt, Silhouettes de Tokyo, Tokyo: Hosei University Publishing, 1954

Tatsuaki Tanaka, Bruno Taut, Tokyo: Chuokoron-sha, 2012

Türk-Nippon Dostluğunun Sonrasiz Hâtirasi Er-tuğrul, Tokyo: Turkish Embassy in Japan, 1937

Credit and Courtesy

Front cover photo, Photography by Ryusuke Yonezawa.

Back cover photo, Photography by Yumi Hosono

Hachiko's illustration and silhouette, Alice McDonald.

Figure 1, Courtesy of the Wayback machine.

Figure 2, Courtesy of Wikimedia Commons.

Figure 3, 6, 7, 8, 12, Photography by Ryusuke Yonezawa.

Figure 4, Courtesy of Yumi Hosono.

Figure 5, 9, 15, Photography by Yumi Hosono.

Figure 10, Courtesy of *Shibuya Meibutsu.*

Figure 11, Courtesy of The Turkish Memorial and Museum in Kushimoto town, Wakayama Prefecture.

Figure 13, Courtesy of the book *The Ship Ertuğrul* published by Turkish embassy in Japan in 1937.

Figure 14, Courtesy of the American Foundation for the Blind Archives, Photography by United Press Associations.